AN INTRODUCTION TO
LIGHT IN ELECTRONICS

Other Titles of Interest

AN INTRODUCTION TO LIGHT IN ELECTRONICS

by

F. A. WILSON
C.G.I.A., C.Eng., F.I.E.E., F.I.Mgt.

BERNARD BABANI (publishing) LTD
THE GRAMPIANS
SHEPHERDS BUSH ROAD
LONDON W6 7NF
ENGLAND

Please Note

© 1994 BERNARD BABANI (publishing) LTD

First Published — July 1994

British Library Cataloguing in Publication Data
Wilson, F. A.
    Introduction to Light in Electronics
    I. Title
    621.36

ISBN 0 85934 359 6

Printed and bound in Great Britain by Cox & Wyman Ltd, Reading

Preface

Nature and Nature's laws lay hid in night:
God said, Let Newton be! *and all was light.*
Alexander Pope, 1688-1744

Light is everywhere and always has been. It is so much taken for granted that most of us know little about it and even the experts are still struggling with the many gaps in their knowledge. We can produce light, we can see the results of light, we even use it for worldwide communications, yet we are still uncertain about some of its hows, whys and wherefores. Not so many years ago, because light travels through empty space, scientists of the day believed in the existence of an all-pervasive medium which they called the *ether*. However nobody could detect it and now we know why — it wasn't there! Nowadays we are wiser, we know much more about the electromagnetic wave, how to generate it, how to control it and how to use it. Yet when it comes to the escapades of light we find there is much left to learn for unfortunately, right up to the present time, despite the brilliant work of early and contemporary scientists, there are conspicuous gaps in our knowledge of the complete process. Nevertheless with this book we can at least improve on what we do know, especially as it affects modern electronics and now that light has entered the electronic communications scene in a big way, it is essential that we get to understand a little about it. The book has therefore been written to throw a little light on a somewhat formidable subject.

Marconi first bridged the Atlantic with radio waves, then of a mere 200 kilohertz. Since then for communication we have moved up the frequency scale through megahertz and microwaves and are now probing light waves — what next? Accordingly no self-respecting electronics engineer can afford not to be conversant with light and its uses in electronics since development of opto-electronic devices and communication systems is proceeding at a truly explosive rate.

The book is not for the expert but neither is it for the completely uninitiated. It is assumed that the reader has some basic knowledge of electronics, however so that the moderately proficient reader is not sidetracked by simple explanations of fundamentals, several are relegated to the Appendices. Chapter 1 however contains revision of relevant electronics fundamentals and it is suggested that even the more experienced readers may gain from some reminders. The mathematics do not go beyond the simple equation. Note that SI units and Scientific Notation are explained in Appendix 1.

F. A. Wilson

Contents

Chapter 1

FUNDAMENTALS FIRST

In early days many facets of the universe were explained by mysticism or even by religion which got us nowhere in gaining a true understanding of what makes life tick. As far as light is concerned it was not until the early seventeen hundreds that Sir Isaac Newton, the English mathematician and physicist, wrote about his studies of light and how a prism could be used to separate white light into the colours of the rainbow. He certainly set the ball rolling for many scientists have since followed in his footsteps, increasing our knowledge of light until the present time when it is no longer regarded only as something by which we see but also, to quote two examples only, as a means of transmitting enormous quantities of information across the oceans and even for charging the batteries of our satellites.

It is essential that we first appreciate those electronic fundamentals on which the theories of light rest. We cannot of course become experts but at least we may generate some worldly wisdom concerning our subject which is one of the most all pervading requisites of life. In doing so we will be obliged to accept without query some of the phenomena and rules which Nature has provided. There can be no explanation as to how or why but at least we have learned how to harness them. One of the most important is *charge* which is discussed next.

Just a reminder before we get involved. Both infinitesimally small and also large quantities are involved in getting to grips with the escapades of light. To quote perhaps the best known example, light travels a distance of three hundred million metres in only one second. This is equivalent to encircling the earth about 7 times in *one second*. How can we as human beings really appreciate such a speed when our fastest aircraft would take days to circle the earth only once? At the other end of the scale we hardly have the capacity to appreciate something so small as is the atom let alone its even smaller constituents. Happily by using

Scientific Notation (Appendix 1) we can take this in our stride so that there should be little discouragement in our quest for a greater understanding of our subject.

1.1 Charge

Nature has given us two fundamental quantities, *gravity* and *charge*. Gravity we know only too well, it is that peculiar attraction two bodies have for each other. Generally one of the bodies is the earth, hence anything else around is attracted to it. This is how Nature keeps everything together. The *force* of gravity can be experienced even though gravity itself is never seen. In a way charge is similar, it too is unseen yet can be extremely powerful. However charge is a completely separate phenomenon from gravity and is in fact the driving force of electricity. In a few words we might describe charge as a powerful but invisible certain something possessed only by atomic particles.

Unlike gravity which is a force of attraction only, charges are of two different kinds labelled *positive* and *negative* and two adjacent charges can either attract or repel each other according to the rule:

"like charges repel, unlike attract"

and the force between them varies as their product divided by the *square* of the distance separating them.

Charge is given the symbol Q and the unit of charge is the *coulomb* which is the quantity of charge transported in one second by a current of one ampere. The *elementary charge* is that of the electron (see Sect.1.3), so named as elementary because so far nothing smaller has been confirmed. When 6.242×10^{18} electrons are gathered together the total charge is one coulomb, from which:

$$\text{electron charge} = \frac{1 \text{ coulomb}}{6.242 \times 10^{18}} = 1.602 \times 10^{-19} \text{ C}$$

(C = coulombs). The electron charge is labelled negative. Within each atom there are also positive charges. The concept of

charge is very important indeed because most electrical phenomena arise from charges at rest or in motion.

1.2 Energy

Here we meet another of Nature's well-laid plans, that by
which we and everything else which moves, does so. Energy is
the most fundamental, it is the *prime mover*. Again, as with
charge, we find that energy does not exist in any material
sense yet it is something which has the capacity for doing
work. In fact work can only be carried out if energy is
expended. Energy is measured in joules (J – see Appendix
A1.2) and because heat is a *form* of energy, it is measured in
the same unit. In the scientific world energy is seen as existing
as two different types:

(i) *potential energy:* i.e. latent but capable of action. As an
example, a body may be in such a position that it can do
work by a change of position. In the first position it is
said to possess potential (or stored) energy. We are
however more concerned with *electric potential energy*
which is most easily understood from the charging of a
capacitor. Clearly while charging, energy is being
supplied and it becomes stored in the electric field
between the plates. Its capability of action is shown in
that if a resistance is then connected to the terminals of
the capacitor, the energy within the capacitor is able to
drive a current through the resistance.

(ii) *kinetic energy:* is that of motion and it is of great
importance in the study of electronics because electrons
are always on the move. The kinetic energy of a moving
body depends only on its mass and its velocity, i.e.

$$\text{kinetic energy, } E = 1/2\, mv^2 \text{ joules}$$

where m is in kilograms and v in metres per second. We
look at kinetic energy in greater detail in Section 1.2.3.

1.2.1 The Electron-Volt

When we consider energies of small particles such as atoms and
electrons, it becomes evident that the joule is rather a large

unit. Accordingly in such calculations a more appropriate unit is used, known as the *electron-volt* (symbol eV). This is the work done or on the other hand, the energy gained by a single electron when acted on by an electric field and so accelerated through a potential difference of one volt. All very complicated but it does result in a more practical unit of energy for this type of investigation and here it is important to note that the electron-volt is a unit of energy, not voltage as the name might imply. The charge (e) on an electron is equal to 1.602×10^{-19} C (Sect.1.1) and since work done $= e \times$ V where V is the electric field voltage through which the electron is accelerated (1V), then:

$$1 \text{ eV} = 1.602 \times 10^{-19} \times 1 \text{ coulomb-volts, i.e. joules.}$$

The advantages of using the electron-volt to express an energy level instead of the joule in analysis of atomic phenomena becomes evident in the later chapters.

1.2.2 The Quantum

Newton and his contemporaries evolved the theory that light consisted of tiny particles which they called *corpuscles*. These were supposed to bounce off objects and so the phenomenon of reflection was explained (Sect.3.3.1). However the theory was unable to explain refraction (Sect.3.3.2). Such ideas then gave way to the one of wave motion which seemed to explain refraction satisfactorily. However at the turn of the last century Max Planck (a German scientist) introduced his now famous *quantum theory*, proposing that there is a fundamental indivisible unit or *packet* of energy known as a *quantum*. According to this theory, light does not consist of continuous waves as we might expect from our knowledge of radio waves but in fact comprises separate quanta, however in the case of electromagnetic radiation (especially of light), called *photons* (see Sect.2.2).

Things may get rather confusing here because in 1924 Louis Victor de Broglie (a French physicist) proposed that any moving object has a wave motion associated with it. We will not get involved with this theory except for the conclusion which is that particles (such as photons) behave like

4

waves and equally waves behave like particles. This idea need
quite a stretch of the imagination but it can be considered
mathematically with success and much experimental work
finds in its favour. The theory does hold good where earlier
theories were in difficulty in explaining things at atomic level.

Max Planck also suggested that energy for example in the
form of light can be radiated or absorbed only at certain
discrete values (this is where the electron-volt enters the scene).
He gave us his constant for use in the simple formula for a
single burst or packet of energy, the quantum.

$$\text{Quantum energy}, E = h \times f$$

where h is the Planck constant of value 6.626×10^{-34} joule-
seconds and f is the frequency of the radiation.

The formula looks simple enough but it must be admitted
that overall, quantum theory is not the easiest of concepts to
grasp. Take heart – we need not get involved too deeply.

1.2.3 The Energy of Motion

Energy associated with the movement of an object is labelled
kinetic as explained in Section 1.2. Having also defined the
electron-volt, we can now go one step further in understanding
this type of energy especially as it affects atomic particles such
as electrons. The mass of an electron is 9.1095×10^{-31} kilograms. This is more correctly known as its *rest* mass because
as Albert Einstein (the famous Swiss-German theoretical
physicist) has shown, mass and energy are related and in fact
the mass of an object increases as its velocity increases. The
relationship between mass and energy is summed up by the
fundamental but simple equation:

$$E = mc^2$$

where c is the speed of electromagnetic waves (Sect.1.4.2).

Accordingly as the speed of an object increases, then its
kinetic energy (E) also increases so that an increase in mass
is produced equal to E/c^2. However c^2 is an extremely
large number (some 9×10^{16} m/s) so that the speed has to
approach that of light before the change in mass becomes

noticeable. People had difficulty in believing Einstein when he made the pronouncement but its validity is not now in any doubt. That mass and energy are interrelated is shown by the nuclear bomb which is capable of taking a small amount of mass and changing it into such energy that the devastation created by its release is indescribable. Any correction required here however is so small that we need not include it.

Suppose an electron is moving with a kinetic energy (E) of 10.2 eV (this is a practical value as we will see later). From the formula for kinetic energy given in Section 1.2 therefore:

$$v^2 = 2E/m$$

Now 10.2 eV is equivalent to $1.602 \times 10^{-19} \times 10.2$ joules, hence the electron speed:

$$v^2 = \frac{2 \times 1.602 \times 10^{-19} \times 10.2}{9.1095 \times 10^{-31}} = 3.588 \times 10^{12}$$

i.e. $$v = 1.89 \times 10^6 \text{ m/s,}$$

i.e. approaching 2,000 kilometres *per second*. Considering that this is happening in an infinitesimally small space, this is a velocity far beyond human comprehension.

From the formula it is evident that if a body reduces its speed then it can do work, e.g. if it slows from v_f to v_s, the amount of work available is equal to $1/2m \ (v_f^2 - v_s^2)$, m remaining constant. Equally if energy is added to a moving body, its speed increases.

1.3 The Atom

Although atoms have always been with us, how they functioned in life was a mystery until Sir J. J. Thomson (the English physicist) discovered the electron about one hundred years ago. His apparatus consisted of an evacuated glass tube with metal plates (the electrodes) sealed into the ends. An electric current could be made to flow across the space between the electrodes. By using in addition a glass plate coated with zinc sulphide within the tube and studying the glow produced on the plate, Thomson was able to demonstrate that a stream of particles was being ejected from the negatively charged electrode and it flowed along the tube to the positively charged electrode. He continued his investigation by installing a light paddle wheel inside the tube and when current was flowing the wheel rotated, from which he concluded that the stream of rays consisted of particles. The electrons had demonstrated both their dexterity and their invisibility. But where did they come from?

Further reasoning as to where the electrons were when no current was flowing led to the fact that they must have come from inside atoms because all elements (e.g. the copper wires connecting the battery to the tube electrodes) consist of atoms only. Subsequently bit by bit the structure of the atom was revealed through the work of Lord Ernest Rutherford (a New Zealand physicist). In a vacuum chamber he directed a stream of alpha particles (these are emitted by certain radioactive substances such as radium) against a thin gold-foil sheet and found that most particles passed straight through the gold foil although a small number was deflected. From this he concluded that most of each and every atom was empty space.

More experimental work indicated that electrons were circling the nucleus in almost the same way as our planets orbit the sun. Only less than one ten-thousandth of the total space occupied by a single atom seemed to be required for the nucleus. It was also found that this tiny centre portion accounts for most of the mass of the atom and also contains a positive charge sufficient to balance exactly the net negative charge of the electrons so that an electrically undisturbed atom exhibits no charge. All credit must go to Lord Rutherford and his contemporary experimenters for their studies of the atom and for picturing it as they did for their work formed the basis of our knowledge today. They had little equipment to help and the irony of it all is that based on the development of electronics since their days, we now have electron microscopes with magnifications exceeding one hundred million with which clusters of atoms can actually be seen.

1.3.1 Electrons in Orbit

As demonstrated earlier (Sect.1.2.3) electrons move at an unprecedented and almost unbelievable high speed of over one thousand kilometres per second, at this point therefore any analogy with the sun and earth fails because the earth takes a whole year to circle the sun once. We must accept that the atom is a most complicated entity but all we need to know here is how electrons become electricity. Let us take the copper atom as an example for this is one of the metals much used when electric current has to flow. Figure 1.1 pictures

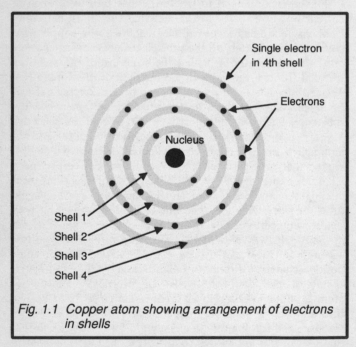

Fig. 1.1 *Copper atom showing arrangement of electrons in shells*

the copper atom in all simplicity and in no way to scale. Note also that the figure represents a spherical volume, not just a flat circle as shown and that orbits are more likely to be ellipses. Nobody has yet been able to look inside an atom and even if it were possible, as we have seen, the electrons move so fast that to us they would be invisible, moreover they are actually spinning as they move. To make matters even more difficult to visualize, the atoms themselves vibrate. Hence the figure can only give us some conception of the mechanisms involved yet hopefully, sufficient for an appreciation of what goes on when an electric current flows.

There are over 90 elements, each with its atoms different from all others especially in the number of electrons per atom. For example hydrogen is an element, its atoms having one electron each, copper as we see in Figure 1.1 has 29 electrons and at the opposite end of the scale, there are nobelium and lawrencium with 102 and 103 electrons respectively. Note from the figure that the electrons are arranged within *shells*. The shell indicates that the electrons do not follow a well defined orbit, however they do remain within predictable distances from the nucleus, the net effect being a three dimensional cloud or to use the more common term, a shell.

Copper happens to be a well organized atom in that its inner shells have the full number of electrons, i.e. 2, 8 and 18 as shown. However not all elements have their shells filled completely. We see that the fourth shell of copper is not complete, it contains a single electron only. It is this particular electron in which we are interested because it experiences the least attractive force from the nucleus because of its greater distance and the shielding from the nucleus by the inner shells. Accordingly this electron in the outer orbit of the copper atom is easily disengaged and can therefore become a current carrier for it is as we have seen, a minute electrical charge. An insignificant value of charge of course but many millions of electrons can be freed together by the attraction of a nearby positive charge and thus become an electrical current. When an electron of the outer shell leaves the atom, the latter becomes positive because it has lost one of its balancing negative charges, the atom is then known as an *ion*. Peculiarly enough an atom minus one of its electrons is also known as a *hole* and this atom together with its detached electron is known as an *electron-hole pair*.

Copper is a material which gives up its outer electron easily, it is therefore a good conductor of electricity. Silver too is an even better conductor. At the other end of the scale there are materials which hold on tightly to their outer electrons so that they cannot be released for conduction purposes; these are the insulators, e.g. rubber, porcelain and most plastics.

So far we have considered the elements, these are substances which cannot be resolved into something simpler, e.g. copper is just copper and nothing else. Elements can combine in a myriad of ways to form *compounds*, usually with completely different characteristics. Take as an example the two elements sodium and chlorine. The first is a silver-white soft metal dangerous to handle, the second is a greenish-yellow poisonous gas. When combined chemically we get common salt, a compound which can hardly be more different from its two constituents. Some compounds have a multitude of constituents.

Let us sum up some of the more important features concerning atoms and their electrons:

(1) each element has a different number of electrons from one to just over 100;

(2) electrons occupy each shell in order but all shells do not necessarily have their full quota;

(3) it is only the electrons in the outer shell which take part in the conduction process;

(4) as a general rule, the more complete the outer shell is, the less the element will conduct electricity;

(5) the electron carries, or rather *is*, a negative charge which we measure in coulombs;

(6) the charge creates a (negative) field around the electron which decreases in strength as the distance from the electron increases;

(7) when another charged body enters this field there will be a mutual force of attraction if the new charge is positive but of repulsion if negative;

(8) current is simply a flow of electrons (*charge carriers*) in one direction and it is measured by the number of electrons passing a given point in one second, the unit of current being the ampere. For one ampere 6.242×10^{18} electrons flow per second.

1.3.2 Energy Diagrams

From Section 1.2 we realize that energy is the all important factor in electronic activity. Frequently the conditions existing within materials are illustrated by means of an *energy diagram* which portrays the differences in energy levels of the electrons in the outermost shells of atoms. Because atoms are packed together, these outermost electrons are disturbed by their neighbours and their original energies change, there is no mean energy level for all the electrons therefore but a band or range of closely spaced levels. The bands may overlap, alternatively there may be gaps in between, known as *forbidden bands*. In the solid therefore no electron has a level of energy falling within a forbidden band.

Figure 1.2 shows in essence the energy diagrams for conductors, semiconductors and insulators. The *valence band* is indicated in each diagram and it is the band which contains the range of energy levels possessed by valence electrons. These are the ones in the outermost shells of atoms which are tied to the atom because they have not sufficient energy for escape from the orbit to gain freedom. On the other hand the *conduction band* is indicated by that part of the diagram which contains the energy levels possessed by conduction electrons. These are the electrons which have been released from the orbits of parent atoms and are therefore available as charge-carriers.

For conductors [see (i) of the Figure] the valence and conduction bands are close together and in fact, for certain atoms may even overlap. Evidently little additional energy is needed by electrons having energies within the valence band for them to break free from their atoms and become available for conduction.

For semiconductors [Fig.1.2(ii)] there is a forbidden band in the energy range. No electrons within the material can therefore function at an energy level within this range. Accordingly for an electron in the valence band to be set free (i.e. to gain sufficient energy so that it moves into the conduction band) it needs to gain around one electron-volt of energy as shown.

For insulators [Fig.1.2(iii)] the forbidden band has widened considerably as shown, hence for a valence electron to become

11

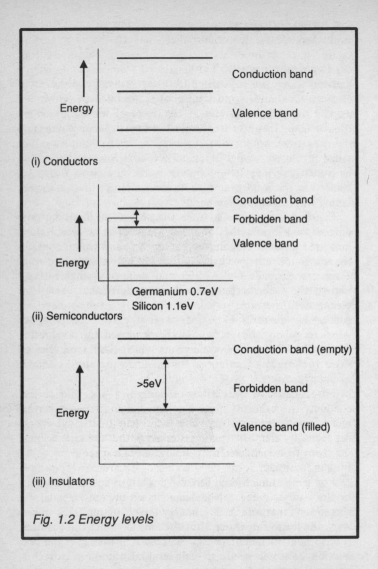

Fig. 1.2 Energy levels

a charge carrier it must be accelerated greatly (for example by an electric field) so as to gain sufficient energy for a jump from the valence band to the conduction band. Clearly this is what we expect from an insulator, i.e. few or no electrons becoming available for conduction.

1.4 The Electromagnetic Wave

It was long ago in 1690 that Christiaan Huygens, the Dutch mathematician and scientist published his book in which he suggested that light travels in the form of waves, and how right he was. However in those early days it was not appreciated that there were other forms of waves having properties similar to those of light, i.e. as we now know, the whole electromagnetic spectrum ranging from long radio waves to cosmic and gamma rays. The visible spectrum occupies only a small part of the complete spectrum as shown in Figure 1.3.

Of interest nowadays is the fact that Huygens in attempting to show how light travelled said: "there must be a substance which is far thinner than the lightest gas, a substance which has no conceivable weight and so fine that it penetrates between the smallest molecules and atoms and that spreads through all space to the farthest star and beyond that. This substance is the *ether*."

Even in the early 1920's the same idea was persisting as shown by this quotation from an encyclopaedia of that time: "What lies beyond the atmosphere in the immense spaces between the earth, the moon, the sun and the stars? Scientists have decided there must be something in those spaces, and they have called it the 'ether' or 'aether'. According to the scientists, this ether of space is everywhere. It is a substance finer than any known to our five senses and it extends beyond the farthest star and penetrates even the densest bodies. Thus the ether enables light to travel through space."

Since then our ideas have changed, we are now confident that no such thing as the ether ever existed and in fact what "extends beyond the farthest star" is simply space, generally defined as "that which is entirely devoid of matter". Even deep down in the atom the electrons move in a vacuum.

Wherever we are there is a host of electromagnetic waves around us apart from those of light as indicated in Figure 1.3. A multitude of radio transmissions is there, all moving past at a phenomenal speed and inducing voltages in any conductor in the path, however most voltages are infinitesimally small.

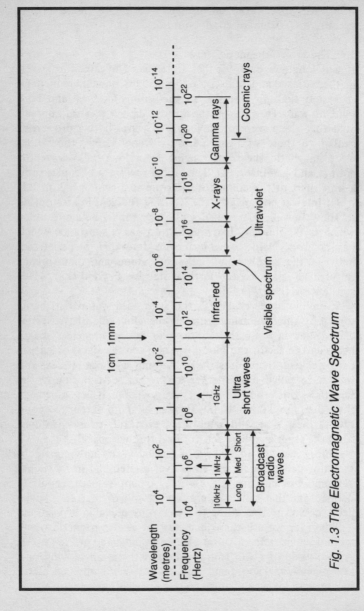

Fig. 1.3 The Electromagnetic Wave Spectrum

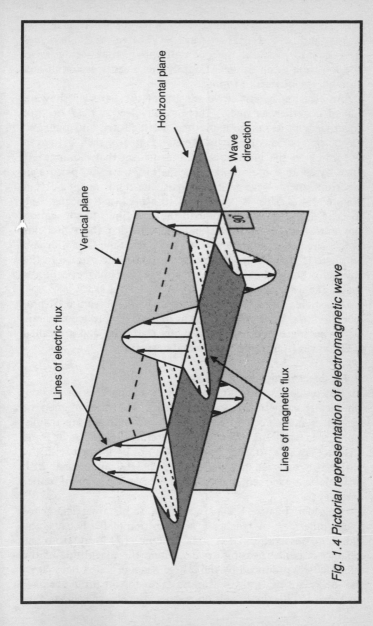

Fig. 1.4 Pictorial representation of electromagnetic wave

Horizontal plane

Wave direction

Vertical plane

Lines of electric flux

Lines of magnetic flux

90°

We design special conductors to pick up electromagnetic waves and call them antennas. Thereafter it becomes necessary to pick out the one radio programme we desire to the rejection of all others. Happily this is easily accomplished through the process of *tuning*.

An electromagnetic wave consists of two parts yet they are linked together as one. There is an electric *field* or *flux* together with its magnetic partner. Both electric and magnetic fields can be illustrated by means of arrows each of length according to the magnitude of the field at that moment. If then by some stretch of the imagination, we could picture an electromagnetic wave as it goes past, the result might be as in Figure 1.4. This is known as a *plane wave* because the electric and magnetic fields and the direction of propagation are mutually perpendicular and we note that the two fields reach their maximum levels at the same time, i.e. they are *in phase* (for phase see Appendix 3). The plane parallel to the mutually perpendicular lines of electric and magnetic flux is called the *wave front*.

For fields vibrating at right angles to the direction of propagation, the wave is described as *transverse*. Electromagnetic waves in space and air are normally transverse and are called TEM waves (transverse electric and magnetic).

1.4.1 Electromagnetic Radiation

In this section we first attempt to gain an appreciation of how an electromagnetic wave is created. The phenomenon of charge is introduced in Section 1.1 and here we are mainly concerned with the effect an *accelerating* charge has at some distance away. At this stage we are not concerned with the difference between like and unlike charges but instead with the electric field emanating from a single charge of either polarity.

Consider Figure 1.5 in which an accelerating charge of magnitude Q at A reaches a new position at B. Because the point of observation, P is some distance (d) away from the charge, it is not possible to determine the magnitude of the electric field produced by the charge when it is at A because of the delay arising from the time it takes for the influence of Q to reach P. By the time it does arrive, the charge is in another

16

position on its way to B. Because Q is on the move therefore its influence at P is delayed by a time d/v where v is the speed of travel.

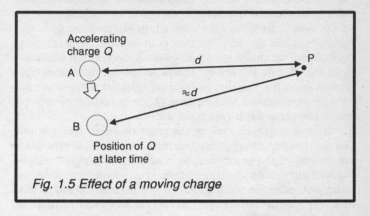

Fig. 1.5 Effect of a moving charge

The full mathematical formula for calculating the electric field at P assuming that Q is on the move is somewhat complicated but we can make the assumption that the movement of Q is small compared with the distance d. A common example is given in radio transmissions where the movement of Q is merely within the transmitting antenna whereas d can be up to thousands of kilometres. We can therefore consider P to be at a distance, d from both positions of Q. Our so-called simplified formula still looks a little uninviting but this is because we are examining the effect of a charge *on the move*.

$$\text{electric field } E \text{ at P at time } t = \frac{Q}{4\pi\epsilon_0 v^2} \times \frac{a(t - d/v)}{d}$$

where a is the component of the acceleration of the charge on the plane perpendicular to d at the earlier time $(t - d/v)$. ϵ_0 is considered later.

The important feature to note is that E is inversely proportional to d, not to d^2 as shown by Coulomb's Law which refers to the effects created by two charges *at rest*. If the electromagnetic wave were to be reduced with distance in the

17

same way (i.e. inversely proportional to d^2 instead of to d), radio transmissions and light would be severely restricted.

The term $a(t - d/v)$ is the *retarded acceleration*, i.e. it is the acceleration at the earlier time when the influence left the charge at position A. Hence the effect of the charge at P is proportional to its acceleration at the earlier time $(t - d/v)$.

For a given Q and v the first part of the equation does not vary, however the second part gives us the relation between t and d. It can be shown that t and d are interchangeable, hence because t must increase (it always does), d also increases. It follows therefore that because Q is accelerating, the electric field moves outwards from Q at the velocity v.

It is all very well making the point that this theory applies to *accelerating* charges, but when do these arise? In fact in the world of the electromagnetic wave most charges are either accelerating or decelerating. Take as an example any electromagnetic wave (including light) based on a sine wave as most are. It can be shown quite simply as in Figure 1.6 that the acceleration of the wave also happens to be a sine function showing that the charges within the wave are continually accelerating or equally decelerating hence are subject to the equation above and therefore are radiated.

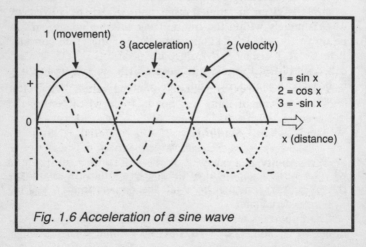

Fig. 1.6 Acceleration of a sine wave

1.4.2 Radiation Energy

What we have shown so far is how an electromagnetic wave is constructed, how it leaves home and that it travels away with a velocity v. However the velocity is usually designated by the letter c but note that this applies only when the wave moves through space (and generally through air) which is clearly its usual mode of travel. We need to find the value of c but before doing so we must get to grips with the two components of the velocity equation, the *permittivity* (ϵ) and the *permeability* (μ) of the medium. When we are considering free-space conditions only, the terms *electric constant* and *magnetic constant* are used instead.

Permittivity is a measure of the ability of a substance to store electrical energy when permeated by an electric field. Here *substance* includes free space and one might be tempted to ask how can free space store anything? But we are not dealing with material things, as we have seen, the electromagnetic wave itself can be considered merely as a travelling *influence*, there is nothing *material* about it. As an influence therefore perhaps we can appreciate how it can be affected by its two other components which again are not material in any way but are simply what we might call *abilities*.

The permittivity of free space (the electric constant) has the symbol ϵ_0 where:

$$\epsilon_0 = 8.8542 \times 10^{-12} \text{ farads per metre}$$

and this in fact is a constant necessary to link theoretical calculations with experimentally observed values. It is clear that our system of units was not in force when Nature did the original design work!

The *absolute permittivity* of any material is given by $\epsilon = \epsilon_r \, \epsilon_0$ where ϵ_r is the *relative permittivity* of the material.

Permeability is a measure of the ability of a substance in setting up a magnetic flux in the region it occupies. The permeability of free space (the magnetic constant) has the symbol μ_0 where:

$$\mu_0 = 4\pi \times 10^{-7} \text{ henrys per metre,}$$

a constant required as in the case of permittivity.

The *absolute permeability* of any material is given by $\mu = \mu_r \mu_0$ where μ_r is the *relative permeability* of the material.

The velocity of propagation of an electromagnetic wave in any medium is controlled by both the permittivity and the permeability of the medium and is given by the general formula:

$$v = \sqrt{\frac{1}{\mu\epsilon}}$$

For free space, $\mu = \mu_0$, $\epsilon = \epsilon_0$. Hence, now using c for the free-space velocity:

$$c = \sqrt{1/(4\pi \times 10^{-7} \times 8.8542 \times 10^{-12})} = 2.9979 \times 10^8 \text{ m/s.}$$

For other media v is lower because both permeability and permittivity are greater than 1. As previously mentioned, in the case of air, the values are so close to 1 that the velocity is almost identical with c.

In free space the frequency (f) and wavelength (λ) of an electromagnetic wave are related by:

$$\lambda = c/f \text{ metres}$$

where c is the speed of propagation.

Our next question must surely be "considering light and heat for example, how can these waves travel the enormous distances such as from the sun to earth, without getting lost on the way?" Again we must resort to the appropriate mathematical equation for the *propagation loss* (α) experienced by a wave travelling through any medium:

$$\alpha = \frac{\sigma}{2\sqrt{\mu/\epsilon}} \text{ decibels per metre}$$

(for decibels see Appendix 2), where σ is the *electric conductivity* of the medium. Conductivity is a feature depending solely on the availability of free electrons so clearly in space where no particles exist, the conductivity is zero. Under these conditions the propagation loss is also zero and in fact areas on earth unshielded from the sun by cloud or mist can receive a continuous supply of heat and light at over one kilowatt per square metre even though the rays have had to travel through the atmosphere. However as we well know, clouds, mist and rain can reduce this amount of energy considerably. From the formula therefore, with an increase in the conductivity of the medium there is an appropriate increase in the propagation loss. Thus only under clear skies can we experience the maximum heat and light from the sun. Put more technically, electromagnetic waves encounter gas molecules in the atmosphere and set these in motion. To do this, energy must be extracted from the wave as it passes.

1.4.3 Interference

We usually consider interference as one thing meddling with another in a derogatory sense. Concerning light waves however the term indicates the combination of electromagnetic waves so that partial or even complete neutralization takes place. Our simple approach to the process concerns waves of the same frequency only and this is considered later in Section 3.3.9. The general conclusion in this Section is that when one wave interferes with another, there is an amplitude change with a resultant phase which is the average of the phases of the two waves. Firstly however we must be sure of what is meant by *phase* so if any help is required, please see Appendix 3.

1.5 Light

In this section we start seeing the light — about light. But let us not delude ourselves that by the end of this book we will know it all — in fact nobody does. Many years ago Dr Samuel Johnson replied to a simple question:

"Sir, what is poetry?"
"Why Sir, it is much easier to say what it is not. We all *know* what light is; but it is not easy to *tell* what it is."

Nevertheless there is much in which we can find interest and so gain a better appreciation of the electronics systems in which light plays a major part.

Light is so much a part of daily life that we may be forgiven for taking it for granted. Yet on looking into it we are in trouble because the complete picture is not yet available, furthermore as mentioned above, even the several chapters of this book can no more than provide an inkling of what goes on. Unfortunately because there are some difficulties with our much-used wave theory, another has arrived, not to take over entirely but rather as a help in explaining certain aspects for which wave theory cannot reach satisfactory conclusions. This is where the activities of the *photon* take over as we will see in Chapter 2.

Perhaps the first characteristic we should appreciate is that light which is an electromagnetic wave (Sect.1.4) travels in straight lines provided that there are no obstructions. This fact was first noticed by Pierre de Fermat (a French mathematician) way back in the mid 1600's. He announced his *principle of least time* indicating that a light ray which is free always travels by the path requiring the shortest time. Chapter 3 shows however that a ray of light may experience many direction changes mainly from reflection or refraction so its complete path is not necessarily always straight.

1.5.1 The Visible Spectrum

The electromagnetic spectrum as shown in Figure 1.3 extends over a very wide range, from about 10^4 to 10^{22} Hz, a range of some 10^{18} Hz, a million, million, million times. Somewhere within this range is a rather insignificant block which as the figure indicates is known as the *visible spectrum*, i.e. the range to which the eye is sensitive. Insignificant as it is on the figure, it ranges over nearly 400 million million hertz and is of inestimable importance. The spectrum extends from about 3.95×10^{14} Hz (red) to 7.9×10^{14} Hz (violet) and is shown in greater detail in Figure 1.7. The wavelength range is from 760 to 380 nm and therefore extends over one octave only (twice or half the frequency or wavelength). All the radiant energy which is visible is contained within this range.

The ultraviolet (*ultra* = beyond) and infra-red (*infra* = below) frequencies are also important in electronics because many light-operated devices work within these ranges. As far as we ourselves are concerned, the ultraviolet can cause tanning

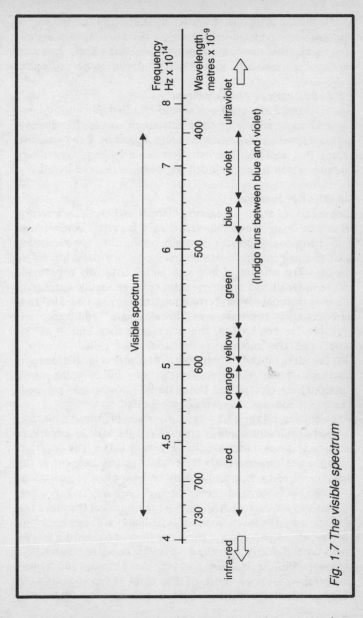

Fig. 1.7 The visible spectrum

of the human skin, better known as sunburn when the sun is responsible. The infra-red region on the other hand is associated with heat and in *diathermy* is beneficial, however excessive exposure to either radiation can cause problems.

1.5.2 A History of Enlightenment

Scientists have struggled for several hundred years to unravel the innermost secrets of light and much success has already been achieved. This is summed up in Appendix 5 and we must accept that although the list there is fairly long, very much research which is not included has been carried out by others.

1.6 The P-N Junction

So used as we are to integrated circuits and the like, a return to a little basic semiconductor theory may not come amiss.

Semiconductor devices generally obtain their conductivities with the help of an *impurity*, added by a process known as *doping*. The amount of impurity added is usually very small, of the order of one impurity atom to several million atoms of the base material. When certain impurity atoms are added to a base material, electrons are "thrown spare" and hence are available for conduction, the material is then known as "n-type" and the impurity atoms added are called "donors". On the other hand, if the impurity atoms added acquire electrons, "holes" (i.e. atoms minus their full complement of electrons) are created and the material is known as "p-type". The atoms added are known as "acceptors".

By joining n-type and p-type materials in intimate contact, the semiconductor diode is created and its basic construction is shown diagrammatically in Figure 1.8(i). The junction between the two materials is certainly not as clear-cut as the diagram suggests, it is more likely to be quite a ragged affair.

Free electrons and holes, being negative and positive respectively, attract each other. At the junction therefore the attraction by the holes in the p-type material causes electrons to flow across and equally there is a flow of holes from p-type to n-type. Many of these charges combine with their opposites on the journey through the junction and cancel out. However since most of the atom is space, others are able to penetrate further before encountering oppositely

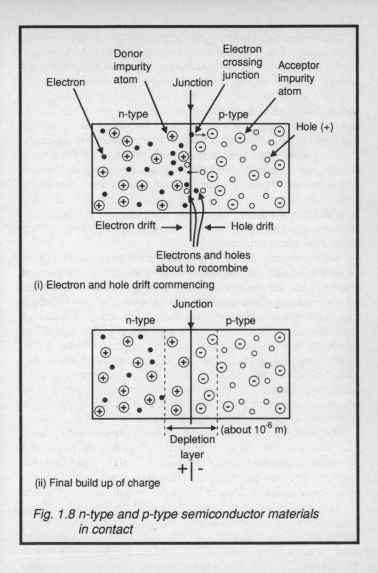

Fig. 1.8 n-type and p-type semiconductor materials in contact

charged particles and so recombining. Charges remain free on average for less than one microsecond.

When electrons from the n-type material cross the junction they leave behind impurity atoms one electron short and therefore positive. In the opposite direction holes leave the p-type material and it becomes negative. This is shown in Figure 1.8(ii). Because on either side of the junction there is a loss of mobile carriers, this region is known as the *depletion layer*. Eventually the charges built up across the junction become sufficient to repel further electron or hole crossings.

The process is a dynamic one because even when the doping is extremely small, there are still millions of carriers (the free electrons and holes) milling around, continually combining and breaking away. The net effect of drift across the junction is such that the potential arising from the charges remaining on each side holds at a level of a few tenths of a volt. This is the *barrier potential*.

Such a single p-n junction is used extensively as a rectifier. If two p-n junction diodes as in Figure 1.8 are assembled back-to-back (in series with one reversed), the standard n-p-n or p-n-p arrangement is obtained — the transistor. These are now available in many different forms and usable in a host of different applications. In particular there is the field-effect transistor especially known for its high input impedance. Many varieties of this type are used in integrated circuits.

Chapter 2

WAVES AND PARTICLES

To understand the interaction of light with other objects it is essential that we master the fundamentals of optical radiation first. This immediately brings us to the bewildering duality of waves and particles, frequently explained away in text books by the fact that light, although usually considered as a wave, may also be thought of as a stream of particles. To all appearances these two phenomena are entirely different.

To get to grips with optical radiation therefore we should at least search for some commonality between the two phenomena. Here we cannot dig deeply into such a complex subject but at least by highlighting some of the earlier observations made by scientists (Appendix 5) and putting them together we may find a link. In this energy and motion reign supreme. Energy we recall is the driving force behind it all. An atom can gain (or lose) energy from various ways, e.g. from heat, light, electric fields and even from collisions with other atoms. When an atom is *excited*, it has been supplied with sufficient energy to move its one or more outer electrons into orbits farther away from the nucleus. This is a somewhat unable condition and in fact most atoms generally lose their newly acquired energy within about one-hundredth of a microsecond. The energy an atom loses in this way has to go somewhere and as far as we are concerned here, it is emitted in the form of a photon.

Much as Planck tried to consider energy as being provided or lost smoothly in the continuous form of waves, his own work disproved this forcing him to the conclusion that energy in the atomic world moved about in discrete bundles or "packets". Furthermore Einstein was able to show that even when a packet of energy escaped from matter, this packet instead of acting like a wave, behaved more like a particle. Accordingly we start by assuming that the energy of light flows in discrete, infinitesimally small wisps, photons in fact. If we are realistic however it must be admitted that in fact we still know so little about light. To make matters worse, no microscope or other device can ever show a photon although we can make it reveal its presence in other ways as will be seen later. But where do the waves come in?

De Broglie set the ball rolling with his idea of *matter* or *pilot* waves. From Planck's and Einstein's work the mass (m) of a photon can be determined as:

$$m = \frac{hf}{c^2}$$

where h is the Planck constant, f the frequency and c the velocity.

The formula arises from $E = mc^2$ (Einstein — see also Sect.3.1) and $E = hf$ (Planck — Sect.1.2.2).

The momentum (p) of a moving body is simply its mass multiplied by the velocity (v). Then:

$$p = m \times v = \frac{hf}{c^2} \times c = \frac{hf}{c}$$

and since
$$\lambda = \frac{c}{f} \, ,$$

$$p = \frac{h}{\lambda} \quad \text{or} \quad \lambda = \frac{h}{p} \, ,$$

i.e.
$$\lambda = \frac{h}{mv}$$

which is the expression for the "de Broglie wavelength"; (h we recall has a value of 6.626×10^{-34} Joule seconds).

The hydrogen atom is the simplest of all with its single electron and from a combination of experimental and calculated data, the electron velocity in the **ground** (unexcited) state can be determined (i.e. when the electron is in its innermost orbit, for all other orbits the atom is said to be in its **excited** state).

$$v = 2.187 \times 10^6 \text{ m/s},$$

i.e. over 2000 kilometres in one second(!), from which the de Broglie wavelength:

$$\lambda = \frac{h}{mv} = \frac{6.626 \times 10^{-34} \text{ Js}}{(9.109 \times 10^{-31} \text{kg}) \times (2.187 \times 10^6 \text{m/s})}$$

$$= 3.3 \times 10^{-10} \text{ metres.}$$

Now it is also known that the mean radius (r) of the electron orbit when the atom is in its normal ground state is:

$$r = 5.295 \times 10^{-11} \text{ m},$$

i.e. about **one 20th of one millionth of one millimetre**, hence the length of the orbit for the ground state (assuming a circular orbit)

$$= 2\pi \times r = 2\pi \times 5.295 \times 10^{-11} = 3.3 \times 10^{-10} \text{ metres.}$$

We see therefore that in this particular case the de Broglie wavelength is exactly the same as the length of the orbit hence the end of each wave must be joined to the beginning of the next. What de Broglie is trying to tell us is that while an electron is moving around the atom nucleus, it has imposed on it a wave motion. This is not easily appreciated from a drawing of the innermost orbit where as we have seen, the electron goes through one complete cycle in a single revolution. Accordingly Figure 2.1 pictures the effect for an excited hydrogen atom the electron of which has gained sufficient energy to be able to move outwards from the nucleus into an orbit of greater radius and containing three complete waves. We might look upon the phenomenon as a wave "guiding" the electron round its path. Note that the 1st, 4th, 7th . . . waves for this particular orbit start at exactly the same point and that the number of complete waves (n) must be a whole number otherwise the wave cannot join back onto itself. n is known as the *orbit quantum number* (see Sect.2.1).

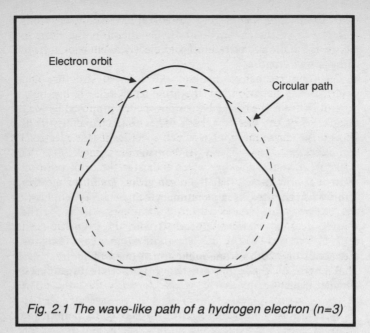

Fig. 2.1 The wave-like path of a hydrogen electron (n=3)

Consider as an example, orbit No. 4 of the hydrogen atom. From quantum theory calculations $v = 5.47 \times 10^5$ m/s and $r = 8.47 \times 10^{-10}$ m. Calculating λ as above shows that there are exactly 4 waves around the orbit, the conclusion is therefore that given the right amount of energy, the electron not only moves outwards from the nucleus into a new orbit but the number of waves per orbit increases. Here we see a particle moving in a wave motion and the link between particle and wave theories begins to show. We cannot go deeply into this for it involves *quantum theory* which is not for us here except for the brief introduction which follows next.

2.1 Quantum Mechanics
So far we have considered electrons as infinitesimally small charges travelling at very high speeds. It is apparently far more complicated than this for besides carrying an electric charge, an electron spins on its axis and so behaves like a tiny magnet with North and South poles. This is rather like the magnetic

poles of the spinning earth. Moreover, like atoms, electrons vibrate. From the energy point of view therefore the electron possesses rotational, vibrational and electrical energies, a truly complicated mixture.

Quantum mechanics analyses the internal structure and describes the behaviour of the atom in detail. It has been developed from the original quantum theory proposed by Max Planck. For the electron, each of its four characteristics is allocated a quantum number which specifies it (the electron) completely. Very briefly these numbers show (1) the *principal quantum number* which indicates the orbit position relative to the nucleus; (2) the *azimuthal quantum number* indicating the angular momentum which in a way expresses the tendency of the electron in continuing to spin; (3) the *spatial quantum number* concerned with the magnetic field of the orbit; and (4) the *spin quantum number* specifying the direction of spin (i.e. clockwise or anticlockwise).

With all this information about the electrons of each element, quantum mechanics is able to unify the conception of waves and particles (even better than we have managed to do in the Section above). The theory is of great help in the study of energy levels in atoms and molecules and in electron behaviour generally. It will be found as we progress that for some explanations the wave theory is eminently suitable especially when radiation passes through space. However when energy is emitted or absorbed we need to resort to the theory of particles. Generally therefore investigations into the activities of light are based on particles, known as quanta but as shown above, in the case of light we call them photons.

Note that especially when dealing with the interaction of light and matter the term *quantum electrodynamics* may be found. Also just to bring us down to earth, it was through quantum mechanics that the holocaust of the atomic bomb became possible.

2.2 Light and Energy

Let us now sum up the various ideas put forward earlier, firstly however making sure that we are fully aware of the reasoning which has led to the idea of the photon. Nowadays in the study of light the photon figures predominantly so we start with a little of its history.

2.2.1 The Photon

It was not until around 1900 that Max Planck began to form his ideas about the nature of light. He astounded contemporary scientists by suggesting that light was emitted in tiny bursts or "packets" of energy. Soon after this Einstein was able to explain the effect light has on the emission of electrons from the surface of a metal — the *photoelectric effect*. Unfortunately this then left scientists with the difficulty of seeing light both as having a wave nature but also as behaving as a particle.

Einstein reasoned that somehow a light beam concentrated its energy on the individual electrons in a metal. For this to happen the light beam had to be made up of discrete amounts or *quanta* of energy as Planck had already shown. Furthermore Einstein considered that all the energy of a quantum could be absorbed by a single electron. As already shown, where light is concerned we call these packets of energy, photons. Einstein's work agreed with that of Planck in that the energy (E) of a single photon is equal to hf where h is Planck's constant and f is the radiation frequency.

Technical books define energy as the *ability* of matter or radiation to do work. It may therefore be difficult for us to visualize energy travelling around on its own when we are accustomed to think of it as that indescribable something possessed by ourselves or machines. Nevertheless the principle of the photon fits in well with modern scientific thought. What is of major importance is that if a photon collides with an electron, the latter may take up the photon energy and the photon then ceases to exist.

Just to develop a little confidence in the photon, here is a practical example:

The medical profession has examined certain molecules of the skin and found that an energy of about 3.5 eV is required to break up these molecules and cause sunburn. The lowest light frequency which produces sunburn is therefore:

$$f = E/h = \frac{3.5 \times 1.602 \times 10^{-19} \text{ J}}{6.626 \times 10^{-34} \text{ Js}} = 8.48 \times 10^{14} \text{ Hz}$$

(Note, E is expressed in joules.) This frequency is just within the ultraviolet range (Fig.1.7), frequencies below this have no effect. Clearly then for sunburn we need the ultraviolet sunlight of summer and this certainly has been proved over and over again.

We can get an indication of the size of the photon by considering for example a fibre-optic system (Chapter 8) operating at 5×10^{14} Hz (0.6 μm – orange/yellow light) with an incoming optic power of 1 μW. Then:

$$E = hf = (6.626 \times 10^{-34}) \times (5 \times 10^{14}) = 3.3 \times 10^{-19} \text{ J}.$$

This is the energy possessed by a single photon at the above frequency. Now since 1 joule is equivalent to 1 watt per second, then the total energy from a power of 1 μW arriving each second is equal to 10^{-6} J. Accordingly the number of photons per second is equal to $10^{-6}/3.3 \times 10^{-19}$, i.e. 3.03 $\times$ 10^{12}. Again, as we so often find when we encounter the escapades of light, a number at which the human mind gives up.

2.2.2 *Photons in Action*
In the atomic world everything is on the move as we see above, hence energy is perhaps the most vital factor. Let us now sum up the various ideas put forward earlier.

When an atom is excited by the provision of energy an electron is momentarily forced into a higher orbit (i.e. one further away from the nucleus). To return to its normal orbit the electron must emit the energy in the form of a photon so clearly the greater the energy fall, the higher the emitted photon energy must be. Planck has shown that a photon is a particle of radiation having an energy hf where h is his constant and f is the frequency of the radiation. From this it is clear that the higher the photon energy, the higher is the frequency of the light and therefore the shorter the wavelength. Summing up, light as we now understand it arises from many millions of microscopic particles known as photons travelling at the speed c. The photons are emitted when previously excited electrons give up some of their energy.

We are told that in space for example, light *always* has this velocity which therefore assumes that when a photon leaves the outer orbit of an atom it must do so at the speed of light. Difficult to appreciate though this is, for moving objects on earth all start from rest, we must leave such explanations to Einstein and his co-workers who have provided a radical revision of the earlier ideas of space and time. Remembering therefore that we cannot ascribe to the atomic world all the laws which we understand so well in daily life, at least we can appreciate that because electrons are travelling around their nucleus at some extremely high speed, the minute pulse of energy emitted (the photon) may have no difficulty in *immediately* attaining its radiation velocity.

Chapter 3

THE NATURE OF LIGHT

So far we have considered that light occupies that part of the electromagnetic wave spectrum to which our eyes are sensitive so it is the stuff that makes vision possible. It also seems to consist of separate packets of energy known as photons. From Planck's work we find that the amount of energy in the photon packet depends on the frequency of the wave. From the earlier chapters we are beginning to realise that the two theories (waves and particles) do have much in common.

The preceding chapters consider some of the underlying features concerning the nature and behaviour of light, some perhaps not easily visualized in a practical way. Accordingly we next bring these features into focus to see how light behaves itself while on the move as it always must be until absorbed.

3.1 Speed and Einstein

One of the scientists' early difficulties was that, contrary to what we on earth would normally expect, it appeared that measurements of the velocity of light always came up with the same answer even when the source of light (or the observer) was moving. Even astronomers found that the velocity of light from stars is completely independent of the speed of the light source. Two American physicists, Albert Michelson and Edward Morley, confirmed this fact in the late 1800's. They were able to show that rotation of the earth had no effect whatsoever on the speed of light relative to the earth.

Albert Einstein then came up with his theories of relativity in the early 1900's. His method of approach was to re-examine the existing assumptions concerning space and time. He concluded that the speed of light is *absolute*, meaning that its value is the same throughout the whole universe. He also produced his *Special Theory of Relativity*. This rather surprisingly shows that mass and energy are related to one another in such a way that each can be converted into the other. His famous equation $E = mc^2$ (in which E is the energy, m is mass and c is the speed of light) looks simple enough but it is of profound importance. Clearly then mass can be changed into energy, proved later by nuclear reactions and on the other hand energy can be changed into mass. The latter is not normally experienced because c^2 is so large that the speed of an object has to approach the speed of light before the change becomes appreciable (Sect.1.2.3).

We can look at this in more detail from a further prediction of the Special Theory that the mass m_0 increases to a value m when at a velocity v according to:

$$m = \frac{m_0}{\sqrt{1 - v^2/c^2}}$$

from which we see that when v reaches the speed of light, m becomes infinitely large, proving conclusively that nothing which has mass can travel as fast as light. Generally on earth nothing tries to do so although scientists have already been able to accelerate atomic particles to such speeds (but only to a fraction of that of light) that allowance must be made for the increase in mass. Hence, although perhaps somewhat difficult to understand, we do have to accept that Einstein's revelations make sense. Thus we see that light is the fastest thing on earth and to our knowledge, everywhere else. It has no mass, hence photons are little packets of energy only — nothing else.

Einstein's Special Theory also predicts that time is similarly affected by velocity with the same formula as above but with the m's changed for t's (for time). Thus time will pass more slowly on a very fast moving object. Arthur Buller added poetry to science when he wrote in 1923:

There was a young lady named Bright,
Whose speed was far faster than light;
   She set out one day
   In a *relative* way,
And returned home the previous night.

3.2 Vision and Colour

For vision we need the eye together with that part of the brain which interprets what we see, a most complex yet fascinating feature of our good selves. One might consider here that we are straying from electronics into medical aspects, but because the eye figures so prominently in the human interpretation of light rays, it cannot be excluded. Moreover within the brain, pictures of what we see are formed by *electrical* impulses — interesting of course but we dare not get involved so we are obliged to restrict our enquiries mainly to the eyeball itself.

A simplified sketch of a human eye showing the major features only is given in Figure 3.1. The eyeball is almost spherical, some 2.5 cm in diameter. Its outer coat (*sclera*) forms a tough protective layer. At (1) is the *cornea* which starts off the focusing process by bending the light rays entering the eye (by refraction — see Sect.3.3.2).

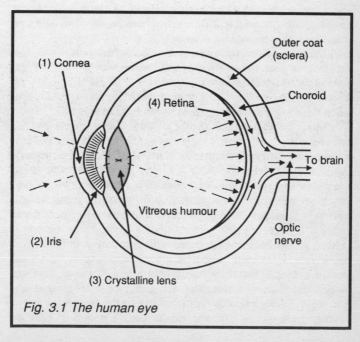

Fig. 3.1 The human eye

(2) shows the *iris*, the coloured part which regulates the amount of light entering the eye;

(3) is the crystalline lens which is held in position by fine ligaments and is pulled into different shapes for focusing. Unlike the camera in which focusing of the image is achieved with a fixed lens and variable distance from the photographic film, the eye operates in the alternative way which is with a variable lens at a fixed distance;

(4) at the back of the eye is the *retina* on which the image falls. As in a camera, the image is upside down. Within the retina are over one hundred million light receptors known generally as *rods* and *cones*. Rods are concerned mainly with black-and-white vision, the cones are sensitive to colour. Light stimulates these nerve-endings in the retina to produce nerve impulses which transmit a multitude of electrical signals over the optic nerve to the rear of the brain.

Filling the space between the iris and the retina, as shown in the figure, is a transparent jelly-like substance known as the *vitreous humour* (*vitreous* = glass-like, *humour* = body fluid). The *choroid* is a thin membrane surrounding the eye and containing many blood vessels.

It is important to appreciate that what falls onto the retina is a host of electromagnetic waves mainly within the frequency range shown in Figure 1.7. These waves are of course neither visible nor coloured; their form must reach the brain for the amazing process of vision to take place.

Colour as Figure 1.7 shows is simply determined by the wavelength. As with our colour television systems, any colour can be resolved into a mixture of the three *primary* colours: red, green and blue. At the back of the eye there are three separate types of cone, each type sensitive to one of these colours. Photons falling on a rod or cone induce chemical changes which in turn generate electrochemical charges to activate the nerve cells for impulses to be transmitted to the brain. Compared with computers and the like, some of our human processes are extremely slow, the eyes are an example for they cannot distinguish between separate images reaching the retina at a higher rate than around ten per second. Technically this is known as *persistence of vision* in that an image in the eye remains for a period of time of

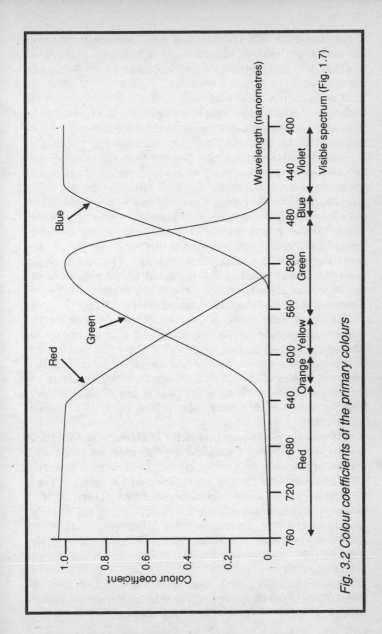

Fig. 3.2 Colour coefficients of the primary colours

about one-tenth of a second. It is this feature which enables us to enjoy films and television in which still pictures are presented to us at a faster rate and because of the persistence of each image, they appear to merge.

The mechanism of colour vision is certainly complicated for although it is easy to say that any colour can be obtained from a mixture of the primaries, there remains the question of how much of each. Figure 3.2 attempts to show this graphically. It indicates how the *colour coefficients* (we might define these as the amounts required) vary with wavelength. This of course is not a true characteristic for any particular person but is merely drawn to indicate the general way in which the colour coefficients might change with wavelength. What is more, at some wavelengths a particular coefficient may go slightly negative but this is not indicated in the figure for it is a complication which is certainly not for us. The colour ranges over the visible spectrum are indicated at the bottom of the graph and as a single example, the graph confirms that equal amounts of red and green produce yellow (at 580 nm).

Reflected light produces colours depending both on the colour of the light before reflection and also on the colour absorption and reflecting qualities of the reflecting surface. As an example, a green surface will appear to be quite different when viewed in daylight compared with fluorescent lighting (even with those lamps which are classed as "daylight") and especially under the yellow light of a sodium-vapour street lamp.

Of interest is the way in which the colour components of a television system are specified for this provides an example of colour mixing which we all enjoy. The colour information (the *chrominance*) has two parts, *hue* and *saturation*. Hue is the colour itself (the dominant wavelength), saturation is its intensity, i.e. how colourful it is. Pastel colours are therefore low in saturation. To complete the information required by a television receiver, a *luminance* or brightness signal is also transmitted, this is especially needed by monochrome receivers.

The colour television camera separates the light from the scene into its red (R), green (G) and blue (B) components by means of filters. Some correction is then applied to account for camera and receiver cathode-ray tube differences. Because the red and green components play a greater part in the luminance than the blue, the broadcast television signal (Y) is assembled in the following proportions:

$$Y = 0.3R + 0.6G + 0.1B$$

the final result as we well know being an exquisite and delightful picture.

Summing up, it is evident that colour is a *human sensation* for what the eye receives is a range of electromagnetic waves having no direct association with colour at all, they are simply on different wavelengths.

3.2.1 The Rainbow

We ought not to end this section without mention of Nature's way of reminding us occasionally of her splendid colours of the spectrum. A rainbow is formed by light playing on drops of water, sometimes on the tiny drops of mist. It is sunlight which has been broken up into its spectral colours by water drops acting like prisms (see Sect.3.3.2).

The rainbow is part of a circle which has its centre below the horizon. Remembering that the sun is behind an observer, the centre of the rainbow circle lies at the point within the earth to which a line joining the sun to the observer is projected. This is known as the *anti-solar point.* Here is proof indeed that we all see our own individual rainbows.

Light rays from all over a rainbow reaching the eye therefore form a conical shape and each one of them is at an angle of about 40° to the axis. Accordingly as the sun descends towards the horizon, the anti-solar point and therefore the rainbow rise until eventually with the sun at the horizon the rainbow becomes semicircular. On the other hand when the sun is above about 40°, a rainbow cannot form.

Finally, do not believe the old English myth that a crock of gold is to be found at the foot of every rainbow!

3.3 Light on the Move

The *principle of least time* is introduced in Section 1.5, here we look at it a little more closely. It is long ago that Fermat produced the idea that out of all the possible paths there might be for light to travel from one point to another, it will always select the path which involves the shortest travelling time. This fact is easily proved. How a ray of light manages to find the least-time path of its own accord is not easy to visualize but it can be demonstrated mathematically (complex notation and probability theory!).

3.3.1 Reflection

We only need to look around us to appreciate just how important is the reflection of light. The grass which appears green or the roof with its red tiles seem so because the material has absorbed most of the light falling on it but reflected the particular wavelengths of its own built-in colour. The reflection of light therefore is not just that from a mirror but it is going on all around us unceasingly. Some special materials reflect light most efficiently, up to around 98%, others such as lampblack reflect less than 1%. This quality of a surface in its ability to reflect light is known as its *reflectance*, this is defined as the ratio of the reflected *flux* to the incident flux. Here we can simply consider flux as the rate of flow of light energy.

Reflection from say, a piece of glass is very difficult to explain precisely by mathematics but it can be done. In a much simplified way we can understand that when light falls on an object it provides the atoms with energy and so increases the vibrations of the electrons. These electrons generate their own electric fields and so themselves act as radiators at the same frequency. In fact the reflected light is not really the original light turned back as we usually imagine it to be, but *new* light produced by a generator driven by the original light. In terms of the photons, as we see in Section 2.2, these are emitted when electrons, previously excited by the incoming light give up some of their energy, accordingly waves are radiated.

This must be a sufficient explanation for our purpose but what immediately springs to mind is the fact that no electron exists on its own, although it is "driven" by the incoming light wave, it is affected by all the other nearby charges which are similarly driven. What adds further complication is that these other charges are affected by the one under consideration – a vicious circle indeed!

For convenience, reflection of light can be considered as:

(1)   *regular* or *specular* (from Latin = mirror) – this arises from a surface which is smooth compared with the wavelength of the light impinging on it; or

(2)   *diffuse* – which arises when the surface is rough compared with the wavelength of the light.

Accordingly a specular reflector will reflect an oncoming light beam without altering its divergence. On the other hand a diffuse reflector has a constant radiation irrespective of the viewing angle. Here we are concerned mainly with specular reflectors, especially the ordinary mirror which usually consists of a highly polished sheet of glass "silvered" on one side with a coating of a mercury amalgam.

Firstly a reminder that whereas we talk of light *rays* and draw neat lines to represent them, this is merely our uncomplicated way of looking at things, it is seldom as simple as it looks on paper.

In considering the paths of light rays, angles are usually expressed at a point relative to the *normal* rather than to the surface which the ray strikes for this may not always be flat. The normal is simply a straight line drawn at right angles from the point of interest.

The laws of reflection are:

 (i)   the incident, normal and reflected rays lie in the same plane, the two rays being on opposite sides of the normal;

(ii)   the angle of reflection is equal to the angle of incidence, both angles being relative to the normal. These are marked θ_r and θ_i in Figure 3.3.

3.3.2 Refraction
In Figure 3.3 the ray of light is travelling in one medium only, usually air. When travelling in a medium other than a vacuum or air the velocity (v) of the wave decreases to:

43

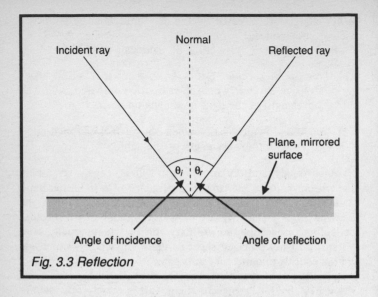

Fig. 3.3 Reflection

$$v = \frac{c}{\sqrt{\epsilon_r}}$$

where $c = 3 \times 10^8$ m/s and ϵ_r is the *relative permittivity* of the medium (for relative permittivity see Appendix 1.2). The relative permittivity for a vacuum or dry air is taken as 1.0, other materials have values greater, e.g. glasses between 3 and 8.

We need not be concerned with actual values, what is important is that the velocity of light (or any other electromagnetic wave) falls on entering a more dense medium.

Consider a wavefront AB containing several rays as shown in Figure 3.4. The incident rays 1−4 are arriving at the plane surface of a denser medium. The incident wavefront is shown at the instant when ray 1 is about to enter the denser medium and it is evident that rays 2, 3 and 4 have progressively further to travel in the rarer medium before they too enter the more dense one. Hence between this moment and the time when ray 4 is at the surface, ray 1 in travelling more slowly has traversed the distance AC whereas ray 4 has moved through

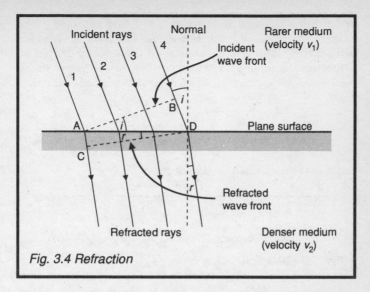

Fig. 3.4 Refraction

the greater distance BD. The refracted wavefront CD is shown dotted and it is clear that the whole wave is bent so that the angle of incidence *i* (as shown for ray 4) is greater than the angle of refraction *r*. On entering a more dense medium therefore a ray is bent *towards* the normal.

In Figure 3.4 therefore let:

$$\angle BAD = i \quad \text{and} \quad \angle ADC = r$$

then:

$$\frac{\sin i}{\sin r} = \frac{BD / AD}{AC / AD} = \frac{BD}{AC}$$

and since BD and AC are proportional to the ray velocities v_1 and v_2 in the two mediums:

$$\frac{\sin i}{\sin r} = \frac{v_1}{v_2}$$

W. Snell (a Dutch astronomer and mathematician) discovered in the early 1600's that the ratio sin *i*/sin *r* is constant

45

in any particular case for all values of i, and he called it the *index of refraction* (or *refractive index*). This is therefore defined for a substance as the ratio of the velocity of light in a vacuum (or in air, the velocity is almost the same) to its velocity in the substance. Using n for the index of refraction:

$$n = \frac{v_1}{v_2} = \frac{\sin i}{\sin r}$$

and it is of interest that, as shown above,

$$v_1 = \frac{c}{\sqrt{\epsilon_1}} \qquad v_2 = \frac{c}{\sqrt{\epsilon_2}}$$

hence:

$$\frac{\sin i}{\sin r} = \sqrt{\frac{\epsilon_2}{\epsilon_1}}$$

where ϵ_1 and ϵ_2 are the relative permittivities of mediums 1 and 2.

Two examples of n are 1.33 for water and about 1.5 for glass, the latter is important to us in the study of optical fibre transmission (see Chapter 8). 1.5 is simply a representative value, there are many types of glass and as many refractive indices.

A well known device based on the refraction of light is the lens, commonly found in microscopes, telescopes, spectacles and cameras. In a lens, rays of light entering the curved surface of the glass are refracted and therefore emerge travelling in a different direction. As an example a convex lens (both surfaces may be imagined as part of a sphere) focuses a parallel beam of light to a single point known as the *focus*. The focusing is entirely due to refraction.

A glass prism is able to display refraction more impressively for it can split a beam of light into its colour spectrum. White light consists of a mixture of wavelengths as shown in Figure 1.7 and as we will see in Section 3.3.6, the index of refraction for most materials actually rises with frequency (falls with

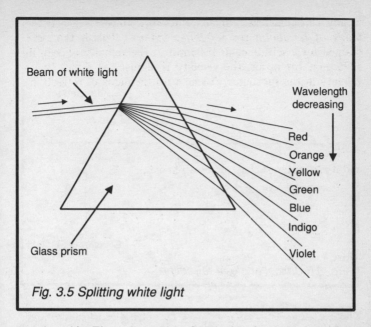

Beam of white light

Wavelength decreasing

Red
Orange
Yellow
Green
Blue
Indigo
Violet

Glass prism

Fig. 3.5 Splitting white light

wavelength). The index is therefore higher for violet light than for red and the bending effect of the prism varies accordingly. How the various wavelengths are refracted to a different degree as they pass through the prism is sketched in Figure 3.5 (of course there are no sharp dividing lines between the colours as the Figure shows). This feature has led to the development of the *spectroscope* from which deductions as to the internal structure of the atoms and molecules of a substance can be made through examination of the radiation emitted when it is spread out into its separate wavelengths as in the Figure.

3.3.3 Total Internal Reflection
Let us take the value of the index of refraction for glass as 1.5 as suggested above. Then for air to glass:

$$\frac{\sin i}{\sin r} = n$$

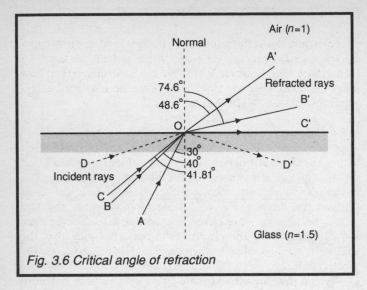

Fig. 3.6 Critical angle of refraction

and for glass to air:

$$\frac{\sin i}{\sin r} = \frac{1}{n}$$

and we can examine the shift in the refracted ray as the angle of the incident ray increases, calculated from $\sin r = n \sin i$. Three incident rays, A, B and C becoming refracted rays A′, B′ and C′ are shown in Figure 3.6 at increasing angles. The refracted ray in each case is determined from the above formula. It is evident that at some value of i, r becomes $90°$ (as in the case of ray C) and the refracted ray travels along the glass surface. Thus for angles of i above this value a ray cannot appear in the air refracted, it is in fact reflected back at the surface as shown for example for the ray D and it follows the normal rules for *reflection*. The surface of the glass then behaves as a perfect mirror to rays arriving at angles to the normal greater than that of ray C, which is said to be the *critical angle*. This angle is easily calculated for when $r = 90°$, $\sin r = 1$ and $\sin i = 1/n$, so in this case, for our glass, $\sin i = 1/1.5$, hence:

48

$$i = \sin^{-1} 0.6667 = 41.81° \, .$$

Total internal reflection is the principle used in prism bino-culars, microscopes and in many other optical devices. Its importance here however is that we can now understand how a ray of light can travel along a tiny glass fibre without escaping from the sides – see Chapter 8.

3.3.4 Polarization
Here we begin to look into the electromagnetic wave itself rather than how it behaves as a light ray. Firstly we recall that all electromagnetic waves have both electric and magnetic fields associated with them, neither type of field can exist without the other. Figure 1.4 attempts to show the two fields and how they are linked in space, now for convenience we concentrate on the electric field only, knowing that the magnetic field is always there and at right angles to the electric field.

The simplest of all waves are those with vertical and hori-zontal polarizations, i.e. the electric field lines are vertical or horizontal. Figure 3.7 shows the important features for a vertically polarized wave; if the electric field points in one direction only, the wave is said to be *linearly polarized.* The three mutually perpendicular directions relating to a wave are shown by the vectors labelled x, y and z as shown at the right of the diagram (a *vector* is a line drawn to represent both magnitude and direction). The direction of travel of the wave is indicated by the vector z, leaving either x or y to show the direction of the electric field (vertical, x or horizontal, y). In an unbounded medium such as the atmosphere or space, the electric vector is always perpendicular to the direction of travel, hence as we have seen, it could also point in the y direction (horizontal polarization) while travelling in the z direction. When for a given wave the electric vector is not constant in its direction but varies randomly, the wave is said to be *unpolarized* (a feature of optical fibre transmission – see Chapter 8).

An interesting outcome of linear polarization is that it is feasible for two waves *at the same frequency* to travel independently of each other provided that one is polarized

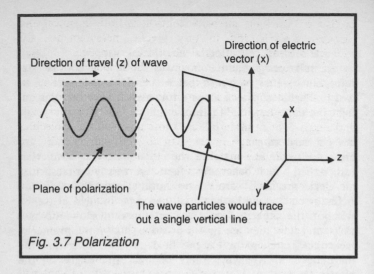

Fig. 3.7 Polarization

vertically while the other is polarized horizontally. In this case the waves are said to be travelling in two different *modes*, e.g. vertical mode, horizontal mode. (Use is made of this feature in satellite television where two entirely different programmes are broadcast on the same frequency — but just to be on the safe side, the reception areas are well apart.)

So far we have considered an electric field oscillating in the x-direction *or* the y-direction. However it is possible that the electric field may have both x *and* y components. If these are at the same frequency and in phase their resultant is simply a component, the vector of which is at some angle other than 90°. Furthermore if the x and y components are not in phase then the electric vector follows a path which varies from a straight line when their phase difference is zero (linear polarization), through a whole range of elliptical paths (elliptical polarization) to a circular one in which the x and y amplitudes are equal but there is a phase difference of 90°. Note that circular polarization is in fact one particular type of elliptical polarization (a circle is an ellipse which has its two semi-axes equal).

In practice polarized light has several interesting uses, there is the commonly seen liquid crystal display (LCD — considered in Sect.6.3.2), light intensity control, in both chemical and physical analysis and in very precise measurements, for example of strain in a material when stress is applied.

An interesting feature involving both polarization and refraction is that of *birefringence* (i.e. double refraction) in which the index of refraction differs when linearly polarized light is changed in its direction within certain natural crystals and liquids. Such materials are those in which the molecules are elliptical in shape rather than circular and generally are arranged within the material with their longer axes more or less parallel. The longer axis for such a molecule is known as the *optic axis* and when the polarization is developed in line with the optic axis the material possesses an index of refraction which is different from that for a direction of polarization at right angles, i.e. across the narrow part of the molecule. Hence the two indexes of refraction.

If next we consider a ray of light passing through a birefringent material, it is clear that the velocity of light will be different when the material is rotated through $90°$. An example of the practical outcome of this is in the use of double refraction to change an unpolarized light beam into two separate linearly polarized beams. Moreover if one of these beams is eliminated a linear polarizer is formed.

The *Kerr Effect* arises when an electric field is able to produce birefringence in a liquid or transparent material. In some materials long molecules exhibit an electric charge, these are then known as *electric dipoles* and generally exist in the material randomly oriented. Application of an electric field results in the molecules lining up to a certain extent and the material becomes birefringent. Hence the optical properties of such materials may be changed by an externally applied electric field so that when a voltage is applied perpendicularly to the direction of propagation of a beam of light passing through the material, there is a rotation of the plane of polarization (the Kerr effect). A suitable liquid is nitrobenzene and the complete device is known as a *Kerr cell*. As an example, polarized light passing through the cell can be switched on or off when a sufficiently strong electric field is applied. If the field is generated by a square wave, the system can act as a light shutter.

3.3.5 Scattering

The process by which a body reflects incident light in all directions is known as *scattering* and it is by means of this that we see what is around us. Here we are not concerned with mirrors which reflect light according to the rules given in Section 3.3.1 but note that even in this case there is a loss of intensity on reflection, i.e. some of the incident light is scattered. This can be shown by directing a beam of light onto a mirror in an otherwise dark room. The fact that the mirror is visible from anywhere in the room indicates scattering.

When a ray of light encounters an atom, the electrons are forced into greater vibrations and these in turn emit their own radiations. If the incident light is unpolarized, the new radiation is scattered. For a material with a well-ordered atomic structure, it can be shown that there is no net re-radiated light. However if the atoms are randomly located within the material then the intensity of the light scattered in one direction is the instantaneous sum of the individual light intensities scattered by each atom. This condition is especially so for gases where of course the atoms are continually in motion.

By much mathematical manipulation it can be shown that the total energy scattered by an atom is proportional to the energy received, a not unexpected conclusion but what is also of interest is the fraction of the incoming energy which is scattered. Again, through mathematics it can be estimated that for air the scattering varies as $1/\lambda^4$ where λ is the light wavelength. From this we see that light at the violet end of the spectrum is scattered to a much greater extent than that at the red end (Fig.1.7). The eye is not particularly sensitive to violet but its sensitivity increases to blue. With the addition perhaps of a tiny amount of green and even less of yellow, the result on looking skywards is the colour we all know so well as *sky-blue*. Moreover, because of this scattering, sunlight as we see it, lacks the blue and violet and it therefore takes on a pale yellow appearance. Then later in the day as the sun gets lower on the horizon so that its rays have to journey over a longer path through the air, the colour changes into orange and finally into red as the sun sets.

Attenuation due to scattering in the atmosphere is termed *Raleigh scattering* after the early investigator, Lord Raleigh. His law of scattering for particles only a fraction of the light wavelength is expressed by:

$$s = k \cdot \frac{(n-1)^2}{N\lambda^4}$$

where s is the scattering per unit volume, N the number of particles per cm^3 and n is the index of refraction.

Clouds are the result of scattered light. They are condensed water vapour, i.e. comprising minute droplets. Yet before condensation the moisture is there but invisible. The question therefore arises as to why the clear air is invisible yet when formed into clouds it is very much visible. The droplets of a cloud are small indeed so that their dimensions are very small compared with the wavelength of light. This means that the group of atoms of a droplet can be considered as being affected by the electric field of a wave en masse rather than at different phases of the wave. This would be the case if the atoms were spaced an appreciable distance apart for in this case the light wave would affect them at different points in its cycle.

Having been excited by an incoming light wave, each atom of a droplet then emits radiation which is scattered. The sum of the radiation for all the atoms is clearly much greater than for one atom alone because all work in phase. The scattered effect is what we see as clouds.

3.3.6 Dispersion
There is a rather complicated expression linking the index of refraction (n) with atomic data and the light frequency which we can reduce for our own purposes to:

$$n = 1 + k \frac{1}{(f_0{}^2 - f^2)}$$

noting that the k represents a formula comprising the concentration of atoms in a substance, electron charge, electron mass and the permittivity of free space.

f_0 is the resonant frequency of the electrons (here we have to accept this concept otherwise things get out of hand, especially when there is more than one resonant frequency) and f is a light frequency.

Here the above formula can be classed as no more than a guide but it is an interesting one. When k is evaluated the formula is capable not only of deriving the index of refraction for any particular substance but also of demonstrating how the index of refraction varies with the frequency of the light — but now we are into quantum theory again.

In our formula above the only variable is f, the frequency under consideration. Under certain circumstances, as this frequency rises we note that there is a reduction in the denominator of the expression above hence the index of refraction increases — but only slowly. As mentioned earlier (Sect.3.3.2) the index of refraction is therefore higher for the higher frequencies of light (blue — violet) than for the lower frequencies (red).

What is shown is more correctly known as *dispersion* because when we study the effect of a prism (Fig.3.5) it is seen to disperse (i.e. send in different directions) the colour constituents of light. In fact the formula used is derived from what the physicists call the *dispersion equation*.

3.3.7 Absorption

Actually the equation used for the evaluation of dispersion in the section above is reduced for our convenience to such an extent that damping of atomic oscillations is ignored. As far as dispersion is concerned, this is justified. Damping is that property of an electrical or mechanical system which reduces the amplitude of free oscillations. It arises simply from the fact that energy is extracted from the system and dissipated usually in the form of heat (e.g. in the brakes of a car). By taking damping into consideration in the formula of Section 3.3.6, we end up with a *complex* equation. We will not get involved for fear of getting bogged down in mathematics but it can be shown that the index of refraction has both real and imaginary parts. To help a little the division between these two parts of a complex number is explained in essence in

Appendix 4. Here the real part shows that as a light wave travels through a material it is reduced in amplitude; this process is called *absorption*. When considering the same process in for example line or radio transmission, it is known as *attenuation*. Of course without absorption or attenuation, things would go on for ever!

The absorption of light as is well known, varies greatly with different materials. With glass for example, the absorption is very small so that light passes through plentifully. On the other hand if the frequency of the light happens to be close to the natural frequency of the electrons in the material, then the index of refraction becomes more imaginary and the absorption of light is greatly increased.

Generally a beam of light propagates in a medium at a lower speed than its speed in a vacuum. The intensity of light falls as it progresses through a medium due to absorption and also from scattering (Sect.3.3.5). Certain materials absorb light more or less equally irrespective of wavelength, other materials absorb certain wavelengths considerably more than others, i.e. they exhibit selective absorption.

3.3.8 Diffraction
Take for example, a point source of light casting a shadow of an opaque object onto a screen. It will be noticed that the edge of the shadow is not sharp but rather fuzzy or blurred. Within the blurring close examination shows that there is a series of dark and light bands. These fringes are the result of a slight bending of the light rays as they pass the object casting the shadow. The bending is known as *diffraction*. This is contrary to what we generally know about electromagnetic waves in that they *are* able to bend, albeit only slightly. Diffraction occurs when edges or corners of boundaries are traversed by a wave of much shorter wavelength than the size of the boundary and considering that even at the red end of the light spectrum wavelengths are less than one micrometre, this condition is normally present.

Christiaan Huygens (the Dutch scientist) explained this phenomenon based on the idea of light travelling in the form of waves. He suggested that every point on a wavefront could be considered as a point source of secondary *wavelets* which

55

spread out in all directions, the wavefront at any time being the envelope of the wavelets. This is effectively saying that the clear-cut lines we use for illustrating light waves should really have frayed or fluffy edges.

A *diffraction grating* consists of a glass plate on which are scribed (or scratched) very fine lines close together and equally spaced hence alternating with unscribed or clear glass. The clear parts act as very narrow slits and diffract light which passes through them. The various wavelengths are diffracted differently hence passing white light through a diffraction grating produces a spectrum as in the case of light passing through a prism (Fig.3.5).

3.3.9 Interference

This is the term used when light waves having different phases combine and so result in complete or partial cancellation. As an example, the waves reinforce when the peaks coincide, alternatively they cancel when the peaks of one wave coincide with the troughs of the other. From this it is clear that if the two interfering light waves illuminate a screen, bright bands of light are produced where waves are in phase, dark bands where they are in antiphase. Phases in between are best considered as follows. To make life easier let us consider two interfering waves of the same amplitude, A (the mathematics get a little more complicated when the amplitudes are different). Let the first wave be expressed by $A \cos (\omega t + \phi_1)$ and the second by $A \cos (\omega t + \phi_2)$, where $\omega = 2\pi \times$ frequency. This shows that the two waves have a phase difference of $(\phi_1 - \phi_2)$. Mixing the two waves therefore produces:

$$A [\cos (\omega t + \phi_1) + \cos(\omega t + \phi_2)]$$

which can be resolved into:

$$2A \cos[\omega t + 1/2(\phi_1 + \phi_2)] \cos 1/2(\phi_1 - \phi_2)$$

(see Appendix A1.5 for help with the trigonometry if required).

This therefore indicates that when two waves of the same frequency interfere they result in a new wave having the same

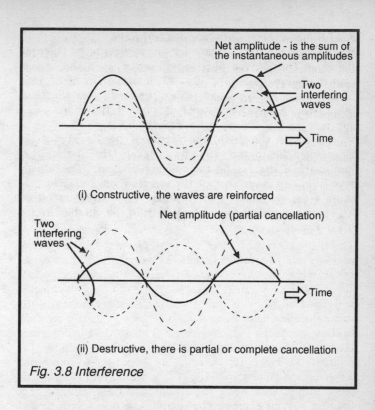

Fig. 3.8 Interference

frequency and having a higher amplitude than that of the component waves. As the last term shows there is a new phase shift which is the average of the phases of the interfering waves.

Generally interference between waves of the same frequency is divided into two different types, *constructive* and *destructive*. For constructive interference the waves are in phase and as shown above, reinforce. Conversely with destructive interference the two waves are not in phase so resulting in partial or full cancellation. The two types are illustrated by Figure 3.8 which now includes the effect of waves of different amplitudes being involved.

3.3.10 Atmospheric Curvature of Light Rays

When it reaches the horizon the sun appears to be flattened slightly. This can be observed at sunset when the bottom edge of the sun looks to be 30 – 40 minutes of arc higher than it truly is yet the top edge seems to be raised somewhat less, overall the general appearance is that of flattening. This apparent rise is therefore higher near the horizon.

The nearer the earth, the greater is the density of the atmosphere hence the refractive index of the air is higher resulting in a decrease in the velocity of light. Accordingly rays from the lower part of the sun are more refracted than those from the upper part resulting in a lifting-up effect. This is clearly greater for the lower part of the sun than for the top.

Chapter 4

MEASUREMENT

When we consider measuring light in all its shapes and sizes it becomes obvious that there are more facets than might have been expected. Accordingly in this chapter we examine the fundamental ideas at present in use from which measurements of light can be made. In the early eighteen-hundreds several scientists tackled the problem of light measurement. Their photometers however had no regard for the different characteristics of light (e.g. colour) but generally were only able to compare two sources on the basis of the inverse square law. As a single example Robert Wilhelm Bunsen (a German scientist) developed his *grease-spot photometer* in which a piece of paper with a grease spot in the middle was held between the two sources of light to be compared. The paper was moved between the lights until the spot more or less disappeared, so indicating that the spot was not transmitting light and therefore the intensity of light on both sides of the paper was the same. Lamps could therefore be compared on the basis that the intensity of each was inversely proportional to the square of the distance of the lamp from the grease-spot. Other photometers were developed, generally based on the inverse square law but differing in the method of balancing the illumination from the two sources.

Subsequent illuminating engineering dealt with the technique more fully and the idea was developed of assessing brightness in terms of candle-power per sq. in or sq. mm. This unit was set up in 1860 as the official standard by which London gas was assessed. The official candle was, of course, well defined. Concurrently other countries set up their own but usually somewhat different standards. Nowadays we treat the subject of photometry in greater depth with international units for the assessment of light fully agreed.

As far as equipment is concerned, most commonly encountered is the photographic light meter which when shown a proposed photographic scene, measures the strength of the light from it. The reading is not in any absolute units but rather as the exposure required by a particular film emulsion. Many measurements of light rely on converting incident radiation into a corresponding electrical signal. It is clear that the power available in radiation is usually extremely small hence noise becomes a problem. Devices used for sensing light which are available for measurement use are considered in Section 6.2.

Electromagnetic waves of light have power to illuminate so it is not surprising that the basic unit is the *watt*. As engineers we are very used to the watt (defined in Appendix 1.2) but when we encounter another unit of power, the *lumen* (see also Appendix 1.2), there may be a little uncertainty. Firstly however we find that the measurement of light is subdivided into two quite different techniques entitled *radiometry* and *photometry*. In both cases the second part (*metry*) indicates measurement. Radiometry is concerned with the measurement of *radiation* at all wavelengths within the optical spectrum, the basic unit of power being the watt. Photometry however is limited to the measurement of light which is within the range detected by the human eye, shown by Figure 1.7 to be from about 380 nm to 750 nm. Its basic unit of power is the lumen.

4.1 Watts and Lumens

The watt is well known to all who are concerned with the practical accomplishments of electricity. It is a unit describing the *rate* of doing work, i.e. the rate at which energy is expended. It is usually considered as being the work done per second when a current of one ampere flows through a potential difference of one volt. This is equivalent to a rate of work equal to one joule per second (the joule is defined in Appendix A1.2). The unit symbol for the watt is W.

The lumen is also a unit of power for it relates to the rate of flow of luminous energy (light). It is defined as the *luminous flux* per *unit solid angle* from a source of one *candela* (see below). The unit symbol for the lumen is lm.

To get the lumen into perspective, some very approximate values of illumination at the earth's surface in lm/m^2 are:

direct sunlight (midday) . . . 10^5

$$\text{dull day} \ldots 10^3$$

$$\text{full moon} \ldots 0.25$$

$$\text{starlight} \ldots 10^{-3}$$

4.1.1 Steradian

Study of light brings with it the need to appreciate certain aspects of solid geometry. This branch of geometry deals with figures in three dimensions, for example shapes made up of surfaces which are not flat such as cylinders and spheres. With the steradian we consider a cone with a base which is part of the surface of a sphere. The slant height of the cone is equal to the radius of the sphere, r and the surface area of the base is equal to r^2. This is illustrated in Figure 4.1. A definition of the steradian is therefore "the solid angle which, having its vertex at the centre of a sphere, subtends a surface area equal to the square of the radius". Note that the steradian is therefore a unit employed in considerations involving point sources of energy.

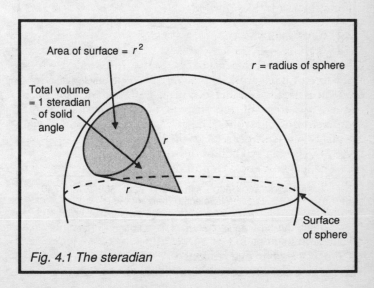

Fig. 4.1 The steradian

61

4.1.2 *Candela*

This is a unit of *luminous intensity*. Its full definition is given in Appendix A1.2 but it must be admitted that to appreciate this, quite a stretch of the imagination is required. It is in fact a measure of the luminous flux per unit solid angle. One lumen of flux per steradian produces a luminous intensity of one candela.

4.2 Response of the Human Eye

Radiometric measurements assume a spectral response (i.e. according to wavelength) which on a graph is flat. Conversely photometric measurements require a detector which has a spectral response according to that of the *average* human eye. A flat response with wavelength is simple to specify but on the other hand a response in any way associated with a human characteristic is more difficult and therefore needs to be

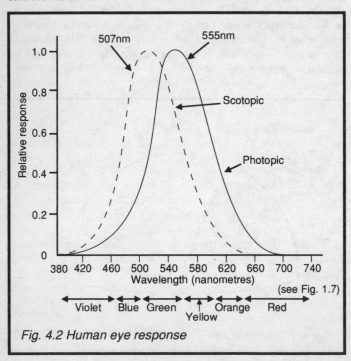

Fig. 4.2 Human eye response

established for general use. Accordingly this was done by the Commission Internationale de l'Eclairage (= lighting, illumination) way back in 1924.

The Commission produced what is known as the *photopic* eye response characteristic, sketched in Figure 4.2. Photopic refers to the vision of normal persons in bright daylight. The dotted curve in the figure is the *scotopic* response, i.e. the vision of normal persons in twilight and we see that this type of response produces an inferior recognition of colour. The fact that there are two responses in the figure shows that the spectral response of the eye actually changes with the level of the light. At normal light levels the response of the eye arises from the cones in the retina (Sect.3.2) whereas when the level of the light is somewhat reduced, the rods take over. The reduced recognition of colour as the level of the light falls is because the rods are appreciably less sensitive to colour than are the cones.

From Figure 4.2 it is clear that the eye is more sensitive to yellow/green than it is to red or blue. The peak response is at 555 nm (5.4×10^{14} Hz) and at this wavelength one watt of radiant power is equivalent to 683 lumens of luminous power. Put in other words, an *illuminance* or illumination of 1 lm/m^2 is equivalent to 1/683 watts of 555 nm light falling on an area of 1 m^2.

4.3 Definitions and Units

(i) Radiometry
This as we see above is the technique of measurement of optical conditions regardless of wavelength or colour.

Radiant Flux is the radiant energy flowing per unit time or the radiant power measured in watts.

Radiant Incident is the radiant flux density incident on a surface. It is expressed in watts per square metre (W/m^2). Also known as *irradiance*.

Radiant Exitance is a measure of the radiant power emitted by a surface. It is expressed in watts per square metre (W/m^2).

Radiant Intensity expresses radiant power per unit of solid angle, i.e. in watts per steradian (W/sr).

Radiance is the radiant intensity per unit of projected area. It is measured by dividing the radiant intensity from a source by the projected area of the source as seen from a specified direction. It is expressed in watts per square metre per steradian. Also known as *radiant sterance*.

(ii) Photometry
This as shown above, is the technique of measurement of light within the range detected by the human eye.

Luminous flux is the rate of flow of luminous energy emitted from a light source. It is also the luminous power, measured in lumens.

Illuminance is the luminous power density incident on a surface. It is expressed in lumens per square metre (lm/m^2) or in lux (lx).

Luminous Exitance is the total luminous flux divided by the surface area of the source. It is expressed in lumens per square metre (lm/m^2).

Luminous Intensity is the luminous flux per unit solid angle in a given direction. It is expressed in lumens per steradian (lm/sr), i.e. candelas.

Luminance is the luminous intensity per unit area arriving at a surface in a given direction (also leaving the surface or passing through it). It is expressed in lumens per square metre per steradian or candela per square metre (cd/m^2). Also known as the *photometric brightness*.

Note that because the steradian is formed on a base of area r^2 then there are 4π (12.57) steradians in a complete sphere. This shows that a point source radiates uniformly over a 4π steradian space. At a distance of one metre from a point source of one candela or 12.57 lumens therefore a spherical surface of 1 m^2 will be illuminated by one lumen per square metre.

We can sum this up so that radiometric and photometric conditions can be compared as shown in the table opposite (measured in the units shown above).

	Radiometric	*Photometric*
Power, flux	radiant flux	luminous flux
Power input per unit area	radiant incidence	illuminance
Power per unit area	radiant exitance	luminous exitance
Power per unit solid angle	radiant intensity	luminous intensity
Power per unit solid angle per unit projected	radiance	luminance

Chapter 5

LIGHT IN ACTION

Truly light is always in action for it cannot ever stand still. It must travel to its ultimate destination then at its journey's end discharge the photons. In this Chapter however we note some of the underlying features of its actions especially with regard to the generation and conduction of electricity – not so much perhaps what it does as to how it is done.

5.1 Space Charge and Work Function

Photoelectric emission arises from the absorption of electromagnetic radiation in the infra-red, visible and ultraviolet regions of the frequency spectrum causing electrons to be liberated from the surfaces of metals and compounds. Before considering this in detail however we should be sure of the way in which two components fit into the overall picture.

Space Charge: this is the answer as to why some electrons, flying around at enormous speeds and in all directions, do not jump out of a material altogether. This clearly does not happen to a great extent otherwise on losing the negative charges of escaping electrons, the material would automatically develop a positive charge and we know this does not happen. The answer is comparatively simple, the relatively few electrons which do escape are held back by the positive charge they leave behind, they therefore congregate at the surface and repel the emission of more. So effectively a few do escape but the *space charge* they set up limits the release of more. It is a dynamic process, electrons with sufficient kinetic energy continually join the escapers while others go back home. Overall an equilibrium occurs and because the space charge is so close to the material, it can really be considered as part of it. Figure 5.1 does its best to illustrate this and note that there is no neat line representing the surface of the material because at atomic level it is far from smooth but rather more like a rocky coastline. It is when we remove electrons from the space charge that things begin to happen.

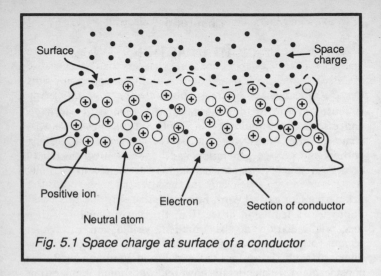

Fig. 5.1 Space charge at surface of a conductor

Work Function: from what is said about space charge above, it is evident that apart from the energy an electron requires for escape from its parent atom, a certain additional amount is needed to enable it to overcome the retarding force of the space charge electric field which as shown above is negative. The energy which must be supplied to an electron at the surface of a material (usually a metal) to enable it to cross over the space charge and to escape completely is known as the *work function* (symbol ϕ). This energy is conveniently measured in electron-volts (eV — see Sect.1.2.1).

5.2 Photoelectric Emission

Generally the emission current (in the form of the liberated electrons) is proportional to the radiant energy incident on the surface of a particular metal or compound. If therefore a photon (see Chapter 2) of energy E acts upon an electron, then an amount ϕ (the work function) must be used in freeing the electron from the surface of the material. The energy left over is $E - \phi$ and this is available to increase the kinetic energy of the electron. Since $E = hf$ (Sect.1.2.2), Einstein suggested that:

68

maximum kinetic energy of emitted electron $= hf - \phi$

where h is the Planck constant (6.626×10^{-34} Js), but note that generally the energies are somewhat less than this because of losses through collisions before and during emission. This formula is known as *Einstein's photoelectric formula* or *law* and an electron so emitted is known as a *photoelectron*.

An interesting result of this which is confirmed by experiment is that when the whole of the energy gained from a photon is expended in providing the work function, there is none left over for accelerating the freed electron. The electron therefore falls back into the material, attracted to the surface which has become positively charged. In this case:

$$hf - \phi = 0 \text{ , hence } f = \phi/h$$

showing that for any particular material there is a light frequency below which emission is not possible. Converting this in terms of electron-volts per electron and also in terms of wavelength rather than frequency we get:

$$\lambda_0 = hc/e\phi$$

where λ_0 is the threshold wavelength in metres, c is the velocity of light and e is the electron charge (Sect.1.1).

An experiment which checks the validity of this hypothesis is illustrated in Figure 5.2. Photoelectrons are emitted from the metal plate on which light is falling. These are able to travel across the space to the collecting electrode. Consider the condition where this electrode is slightly negative with respect to the metal plate. The negative electric field set up by the plate tends to repel arriving photoelectrons depending on the plate potential and the energies of the photoelectrons. When the field is weak photoelectrons with high kinetic energies can still reach the collecting electrode even though it is slightly negative. The number which does so is recorded as current on the ammeter. As the electric field is increased in strength however, photoelectrons with the lower velocities are repelled before they can reach the collecting anode and they are driven back. The collecting electrode voltage which

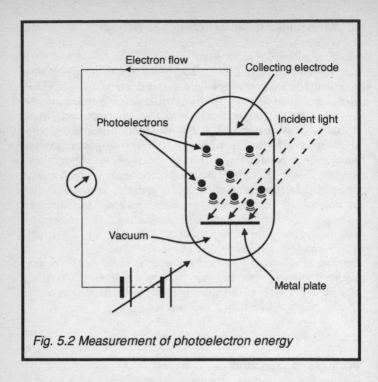

Fig. 5.2 Measurement of photoelectron energy

just reduces the current to zero therefore corresponds to the maximum photoelectron energy.

The substitution of different light frequencies and intensities proves that photoelectron energy is not related to light intensity. On the other hand it can be shown that maximum photoelectron energy varies directly with frequency, for example, a dim violet light at for example $f = 7.5 \times 10^{14}$ Hz gives rise to more energetic photoelectrons than does a powerful red light at say, $f = 4.5 \times 10^{14}$ Hz.

As an example, suppose that the metal plate used in Figure 5.2 is zinc which has a work function of 3.73 eV. The minimum frequency of light which will cause photoemission is therefore ϕ/h which works out to 9×10^{14} Hz. By reference to Figure 1.7 we see that ordinary visible light will not free electrons from zinc but ultraviolet light will.

We can also see what the conditions are at any other frequency, say at 5×10^{15} Hz in the ultraviolet. Firstly the total energy possessed by a photoelectron at this frequency is calculated from $E = hf$ which in this case is 3.313×10^{-18} joules. Some of this energy is taken up in releasing the electron from the surface of the zinc, an amount $3.73 \times 1.602 \times 10^{-19}$, i.e. 5.98×10^{-19} joule, hence the photoelectron is left with $[(3.313 \times 10^{-18}) - (5.98 \times 10^{-19})]$ joules which is equal to 2.72×10^{-18} joules, i.e. about 17 eV. This in Figure 5.2 would be the kinetic energy which speeds the photoelectron across the tube.

For added interest we can calculate the photoelectron velocity (v). From the basic formula, kinetic energy = $1/2 \ mv^2$ (where m is the mass of the electron − 9.109×10^{-31} kg), then:

$$v = \sqrt{\frac{2 \times 2.72 \times 10^{-18}}{9.109 \times 10^{-31}}} = 2.44 \times 10^6 \ \text{metres}/second \ ,$$

a speed far beyond human comprehension.

5.3 Photoconductivity

This is the increase in conductivity in certain semiconductor materials when irradiated. Briefly the effect of the radiation is to create electron-hole pairs (Sect.1.3.1) which then act as charge carriers, the essential requirement for the flow of electricity.

Here we consider light as a stream of photons (Sect.2.2), each being a tiny packet of energy (nothing else, a photon has no *physical* being). When photons fall onto the surface of certain materials their energies are released and, given the right conditions, electron-hole pairs are created so increasing the conductivity.

Looking at photoconductivity from an energy point of view therefore, given sufficient energy from an incoming photon, an orbiting electron in the valence shell of an atom can be freed so creating an electron-hole pair. On an energy diagram as in Figure 5.3 however we see a "band-gap" or

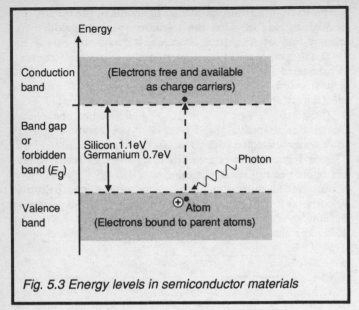

Fig. 5.3 Energy levels in semiconductor materials

"forbidden band" showing that an electron must receive more energy than that indicated by the gap to become available for conduction. It is a fact that for any material, no electrons can possess energy levels within this band. The band-gap differs according to the material, for conductors there may be no gap at all, for semiconductors a moderate gap as shown in the Figure and for insulators a much wider gap making it almost impossible for an electron to gain sufficient energy to jump (energy-wise) across to the conduction band to be available for conduction (see Fig.1.2).

Summing this up, for light to free an electron from its parent atom, the photon energy supplied must be equal to or greater than the band-gap energy (E_g). As shown in Section 2.2 the energy of a single photon is calculated from $E = hf$ where f is the radiation frequency and h is the Planck constant (see Sect.5.2 above). Accordingly, for photoconductivity to occur, hf must be greater than E_g. When this condition is satisfied, the conductivity of the illuminated material increases noticeably.

Here is a practical example. As shown in the Figure, E_g (the band-gap) for silicon is 1.1 eV, hence photoconductivity arises at frequencies at or above E_g/h Hz, i.e.

$$\frac{1.1 \times 1.602 \times 10^{-19}(\text{J})}{6.626 \times 10^{-34} \text{ (J s)}} = 2.66 \times 10^{14} \text{ Hz},$$

i.e. 1128 nanometres (note that in the numerator, electron volts are converted to joules).

This is in the infra-red region and as indicated above, higher frequencies, that is, including all visible ones, are also effective. We can equally work in wavelengths by using $E_g = hc/\lambda$, hence the critical wavelength, i.e. the *longest* wavelength at which photons are of sufficient energy to produce conductivity, is given by $\lambda_c = hc/E_g$. Wavelengths greater than λ_c therefore cannot give rise to photoconductivity and note that this is controlled entirely by E_g for the particular material.

The conclusion is that if photons arrive having energies less than that of the band-gap, they cannot be absorbed to create photoconductivity. On the other hand photons having sufficiently high energies lower the material resistance considerably when compared with its "dark" resistance.

5.4 Luminescence

It is well known that a bar of iron when heated sufficiently glows red and when heated even more the glow tends towards white, hence our expressions "red hot" and "white hot". This is an example of the emission of light when heat is applied. On the other hand *luminescence* is concerned with the emission of light *without* the injection of heat and most homes contain an excellent example of luminescence, the television screen.

Luminescence arises when a material emits visible light when there is some excitation from outside. The lowest possible energy level for an atom is known as the *ground state*, anything higher is known as an *excited state*. Generally atoms prefer to be in the ground state so they are inclined to get rid of surplus energy as soon as possible. To raise an atom to an excited state requires the provision of energy, usually by the application of electromagnetic radiation or other charged particles. An excited atom returning to its ground state therefore must emit the surplus energy and this is done as radiation in the form of photons, i.e. light is emitted.

There are several examples of this, even with living things such as glow-worms and fireflies in which the excitation is provided by chemical reactions. An element which needs careful handling is phosphorus because it oxidises spontaneously in the air and this is accompanied by the emission of a faint green glow (hence the term phosphorescence — see below).

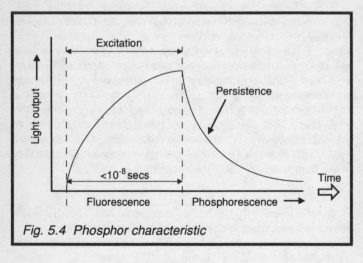

Fig. 5.4 *Phosphor characteristic*

Figure 5.4 shows a typical characteristic of a phosphor which is a substance used especially in cathode-ray tubes. Note that the characteristic is divided into two regions, *fluorescence* and *phosphorescence*. These are two sub-divisions of luminescence depending on the length of time it continues after the excitation ceases. If the luminescence persists for less than some 10^{-8} seconds, then the description "fluorescence" is used as shown in the Figure; if the time is longer, the description changes to "phosphorescence". The term fluorescence applies for the emission of light *during* excitation, it is phosphorescence thereafter.

For cathode-ray tubes generally many phosphors are available with phosphorescence times ranging from a microsecond or less to considerably more than one second. The phosphorescence time is more generally known as the *persistence*. When an electron beam strikes the phosphor coating on the inner face of the tube, the energy of the beam is transferred to the electrons in the phosphor crystals. This raises their energy levels and when each atom returns to the ground state, it emits a photon. This process of light emission decays approximately exponentially for a period of time (the persistence).

The chemical composition of a phosphor is derived from two components, the host material and an activator. The latter is used to prolong the time of phosphorescence but alternatively other materials may be combined with the host material to reduce the time. For example, long persistance tubes are used in oscilloscopes for examination of fleeting waveforms; on the other hand, television tubes require a persistence (to the 10% level) of less than one millisecond.

Light is also emitted when recombination is present in certain semiconductor junctions and is the basis on which light-emitting diodes operate. This is considered in greater detail in Chapter 6.

Chapter 6

LIGHT DEVICES

In this chapter we examine some of the practical applications of all that has gone before in the earlier chapters. Of course one light device which has never lost its fascination is the *laser*, this is a sufficiently complex generator to warrant a chapter on its own and this follows.

6.1 Emitters

Unquestionably the most influential and vital light emitter is our magnificent sun. Because of its splendour and its importance to us all, the sun has figured prominently in early writings and poetry. On a descriptive note William Blake wrote, "when the sun rises, do you not see a round disc of fire somewhat like a guinea"? However less cheerful was A. J. Balfour when he wrote, "The energies of our system will decay, the glory of the sun will be dimmed . . . ". He was right of course but happily not in our time.

The importance of the sun to us is for the constant support of life. It may be difficult to appreciate perhaps but the sun is only one of the many millions of stars in the Universe. We ourselves see it as a fiery disc dispensing light and heat to us. In fact most of its radiation goes off into space, only a diminutive amount of the total sun's energy is received on earth.

The mean distance to our provider of light is some 93 million miles, a short distance when the rest of the Universe is considered. The sun is actually a gigantic nuclear furnace with a centre core running at about 14 million degrees Celsius. There atoms move so fast that collisions produce nuclear reactions. This has been going on for some 5,000 million years and it is estimated that it can carry on for as long again before becoming burnt out.

Refraction of light (Sect.3.3.2) lengthens our days noticeably. Through space the sun's rays travel in straight lines but not so in the earth's atmosphere. Because the atmosphere is more dense nearer the ground, when the sun's rays travel through it at a low angle, the bending of the rays is appreciable.

The rays therefore arrive from a direction that differs from the true (straight line) direction from the sun. The net effect is that the sun is seen to rise above the horizon several minutes before it actually does and at the end of the day it appears to stay on the horizon several minutes after it has actually set.

The sun is the greatest continuous emitter of light in our experience. Some examples of more earthly ones follow.

6.1.1 Tungsten Lamps

This type is described as *incandescent*, i.e. the light is produced by the glowing of a white-hot filament. It is one of the most commonly found types of lamp. Heating the filament is accomplished by applying a sufficiently high potential difference across it. Air is excluded from the process otherwise the filament oxidises and is soon destroyed.

The heating of the filament arises from the fact that the applied potential difference provides the electrons with additional energy, hence their random motions increase with the result that heat, the kinetic energy of particle motion, is generated. Electrons only remain in their high energy states for extremely short periods of time and when dropping back from the higher levels, the added energy must be shed and this is done in the form of photons. For visible light the energy transitions must be within the range say, $1.7 - 3.3$ electron-volts (Sect.2.2.1). Such conditions apply when for a given applied voltage the filament length and resistance are arranged for the optimum filament temperature to be obtained. If the filament temperature is too low, the light output tends towards the red end of the spectrum as in infra-red lamps; if too high, filament life is reduced although light output is high, a technique sometimes used with projection lamps.

For the filament the metal tungsten is used because it has a high melting point, well above 3,000 K; use is generally restricted to a somewhat lower operating temperature, say $2,500 - 2,800$ K. Only about 5% of the radiant flux output falls within the visible spectrum, hence the recent advent of lamps of higher efficiencies, e.g. the *halogen* lamp. The halogens are a group of non-metallic elements such as fluorine, chlorine, bromine and iodine. The particular property they have is their capability of forming compounds with metals, e.g. the metal sodium combines with the halogen chlorine to give us our common salt, i.e. sodium chloride. In fact the group name is derived from this particular compound, i.e. from Greek, *hals* = sea salt.

Lamps of this type have a quartz envelope with a halogen vapour fill. A commonly used halogen vapour is that of iodine. Tungsten filaments slowly vaporise during use, the result being a deposit on the envelope of the lamp thereby reducing the light output. The halogen keeps the envelope clean by chemical reaction with the solidified tungsten vapour and in fact the evaporated tungsten is redeposited on the filament.

6.1.2 Electric Discharge Lamps

Unlike the tungsten lamp, these are non-filament lamps in which current flows through an ionized gas instead of a metallic wire. Gas atoms are capable of absorbing or emitting photons but of a certain energy value only (Sect.2.2.1). The gas is contained at low pressure within a glass tube which has electrodes at each end (see Fig.6.1). If a low value potential difference is applied across the electrodes, only a small flow of electrons occurs made up of the few which gain sufficient energy from surrounding heat or light to overcome the space charge at the cathode. (The space charge arises from the fact that some electrons have sufficient thermal energy for escape from the surface of the electrode but they themselves repel the emission of more (Sect.5.1 and Fig.5.1).) A relatively few electrons are therefore collected by the anode.

If the potential difference across cathode and anode is increased, the accelerations imparted to the few electrons within the interelectrode space increase. Eventually their velocities are such that on encountering a neutral gas atom or molecule, at least one electron is freed by collision. These electrons are also accelerated by the field and cause more collisions. The effect is cumulative but clearly does not occur until the applied voltage reaches a value such that the electron energies are capable of causing ionization by collision. (Ionization occurs when an electrically neutral atom or molecule loses (or sometimes gains) one or more electrons. Loss of an electron creates a positive ion because a negative balancing

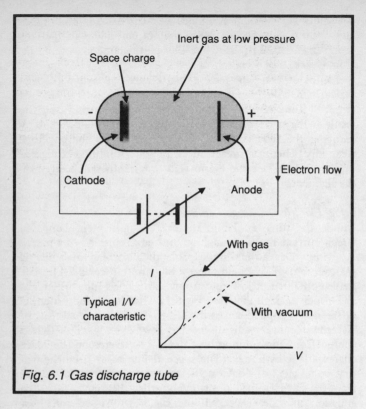

Space charge

Inert gas at low pressure

−   +

Cathode

Anode

Electron flow

Typical *I/V*
characteristic

With gas

With vacuum

I

V

Fig. 6.1 Gas discharge tube

charge has been removed.) However recombination takes place continually and when an ion recombines with its lost electron or combines with another electron, the neutrality of the atom is restored and the energy provided by the applied potential which caused the original break-up is accordingly released − this is in the form of a photon.

Not only therefore does the supply of free electrons increase, some of which form an anode current, but also the atom or molecule ions drift towards the cathode. Here they reduce the space charge by their presence and by removing electrons from it so that they may become neutral particles again. Hence there is a certain value, depending on the gas itself at which the current suddenly rises and the gas glows.

Put simply, at this point a sufficiently high voltage has been applied for the gas to ionize. This is when electrons are actually removed from their parent atoms.

Alternatively because for each gas there are fixed energy levels, light may also be emitted when a gas atom or molecule changes from one excited level to a lower one or to the ground state, in this case no electron loss has occurred.

The whole process is simply that of providing energy to the gas by means of an applied potential with the quick return to this energy in the form of photons. Every gas has its own characteristic glow when this process takes place. Well known examples are the reddish glow of neon which is seen in so many neon signs, and the yellow of sodium as is used for street lighting.

Fluorescent Lamps

There are several different types but in all the light is produced by the excitation of phosphors by ultraviolet radiation. The phosphor forms a coating on the inside surface of a glass tube which has electrodes sealed into the two ends. The tube contains a mixture of argon and mercury vapour at low pressure. As its derivation from the Greek indicates, argon (= lazy or inactive) is an *inert* gas, it is used as a starting gas because it ionizes easily. With sufficient voltage applied across the tube, the mercury vapour ionizes and under such conditions the electrical characteristics of the tube are controlled almost entirely by the vapour. This is known as "gas breakdown". A large current now flows across the tube and the discharge is self-sustaining. Once the mercury vapour discharge is established, a series inductor "drops" the applied voltage to ensure that the lamp operates over its optimum discharge range. Without such a voltage dropping arrangement the tube would quickly be destroyed since its resistance on discharge is low.

Ionized mercury vapour emits energy at around 250 nanometres (1.18×10^{15} Hz). From Figure 1.7 we see that this is well into the ultraviolet range which is therefore useless for lighting. The energy is used instead to excite phosphors coated on the inside of the tube. These phosphors absorb the energy, accordingly electrons are excited to a higher level and on reversion of atoms and molecules to the ground state, the energy is emitted as photons, i.e. the light is now within the visible range.

Fluorescent lamps are available either as hot- or cold-cathode types. In *preheat* lamps the electrodes are heated for a few seconds before ionization of the gas is induced. *Instant-start* lamps are started by applying a sufficiently high voltage across the electrodes while *rapid-start* lamps combine electrode heating with a lower voltage. Efficiencies of course vary but typically a 100 watt lamp might have an efficiency of around 55 lumens per watt.

Sodium Vapour Lamps
These are one of the most efficient sources of electrically generated light, about double the efficiency of the fluorescent lamp, e.g. a 400 watt sodium lamp could have an efficiency of 110 − 120 lumens per watt. Sodium is a powerful alkali metal and when used in a lamp it runs at a high temperature, in fact sufficiently high that ordinary glass is unsuitable for the tube. Even quartz is unusable because it will succumb to the corrosive atmosphere of the sodium. A special tube which does not soften at high temperatures such as *alumina* (an oxide of aluminium) is therefore most likely to be used. The end seals are also of alkali-resistance metals.

A different inert gas from that used for fluorescent lamps is employed for sodium vapour lamps, xenon. As with argon, xenon is readily ionized and when this happens an arc crosses the tube so starting up the process of increasing the vapour pressure. Most of the lamp output ranges between 570 and 630 nanometres which as Figure 1.7 shows is in the yellow/orange colour range. The output falls considerably at wavelengths above and below this range.

6.1.3 Sparks and Arcs
Both these phenomena are the result of electrical conduction through a gas (remembering that air is also a gas). The main difference between spark and arc is not difficult to appreciate, it is simply that of duration. Generally a spark is over within an extremely short time, on the other hand an arc has no time limit provided that the power which drives it continues to be

available.

With both phenomena there is involvement with *plasma*. Plasmas arise in ionized gases. When a gas is made up of positively charged gas atoms or molecules and an approximately equal number of free electrons, it is known as a plasma. The gas then differs markedly from its unionized state, especially in its conduction properties because it now consists of electrically charged particles which are mobile. In fact a fully ionized plasma may have conducting properties considerably better than those of our well known metal conductor, copper. Plasmas are in fact also involved in fluorescent and neon lighting (Sect.6.1.2).

A spark is therefore produced when a gas which is normally a poor conductor is forced to conduct electricity momentarily and in a way the arc can be classed as a continuous spark.

At low pressures within a gas there is initially a small amount of ionization created by stray radiation, especially that of light. Under these conditions, when a potential is applied conduction can take place because the positive and negative ions are able to move in opposite directions. Because gas pressure is low, the electrons are less likely to collide with gas molecules quickly (here we are talking in terms of the tiniest fraction of a second), in other words their free paths are comparatively long and therefore they are able to attain high velocities. When they do finally collide with gas molecules therefore their energies are such that more electrons are released so that the number of positive and negative ions increases. The effect is therefore cumulative, resulting in a rapid build-up of current, eventually leading to an electric discharge which is visible, i.e. a spark or an arc.

A spark manifests itself as a visible and noisy discharge of electricity — we have lightning to constantly remind us of this. An everyday example of a smaller spark is that in the motor car spark plug. The voltage applied is high (several thousands) so that ionization of the gas by collision is produced with the cumulative effect described above. The path between the electrodes therefore becomes highly conducting with the result that the sudden disruptive discharge is luminous, i.e. a spark has crossed between the electrodes. Lightning is our other example but one in which the electrodes (the clouds and the earth) are of enormous dimensions compared with the spark plug. The mechanism of spark discharge is complex and the actual voltage required for a spark to occur under any particular set of conditions is difficult to assess especially in view of the considerable effect of the shape of the electrodes.

Most arcs nowadays are contained within special envelopes but in earlier days such enclosures were not employed. In the first cinema projectors the arc burned between two carbon rods in air with a special shutter automatically and quickly introduced between the light source and the film in the event of the latter jamming in the gate and therefore being exposed to the intense heat of the arc. As the carbon rods burned away, so increasing the arc length, one rod was screwed in by hand and later on automatically by a motor. Little wonder that the enclosed arc was soon developed.

There are several types of arc lamp, one which is typical of the basic construction of many and is much used in the *xenon short-arc lamp*. This is an enclosed-bulb type with high stability and high light output. Also because the electrodes themselves do not burn away, adjustments are not necessary hence this type replaces the carbon arc in many applications. A sketch of an xenon short-arc lamp is given in Figure 6.2. The thick quartz envelope has to withstand an internal pressure of several atmospheres of xenon gas. The emission results in a considerable drop in potential across the tube, in fact even with large arc currents the potential difference across the tube is likely to be considerably less than 100 volts. Xenon is generally used because the lamp then has a high and fairly constant output of white light (with some in the infra-red). Typically the electrodes are of tungsten and the lamp starts up quickly (within one or two seconds). Arc lengths vary from a fraction of one millimetre to over 15 mm. Efficiency of this type of lamp is high at around 40 – 50 lumens per watt. Most lamps run at about 1,000 watts upwards.

A second type of short-arc lamp but one with a longer warm-up time operates with mercury vapour. This disadvantage of comparatively long warm-up is overcome to a certain extent by the addition of xenon gas. Generally this type of

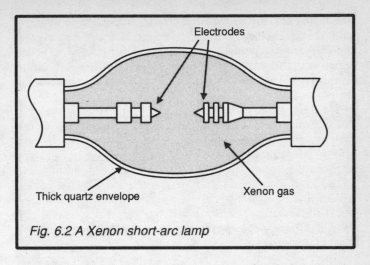

Fig. 6.2 A Xenon short-arc lamp

lamp has a slightly higher efficiency than for the pure xenon type but with a less smooth light output/wavelength characteristic.

6.1.4 Light-Emitting Diodes

These operate on the principle that under forward bias conditions in a p-n junction diode (positive to p, negative to n — Sect.1.6) electrons fed into the n-type material are easily driven by the electric field into the p-type via the reduced depletion layer (see Fig.1.8). Once within the p-type but still near the junction these electrons which have energies within the conduction band meet a good supply of holes with energies in the valence band. Recombination therefore takes place and from Figure 6.3 it is clear that an electron in moving down to the lower energy level must emit its surplus energy. This is in the form of a photon of radiation.

The wavelength of a photon is obtained from Planck's formula as follows. We use the more common gallium arsenide (GaAs) as an example — this has a band-gap energy of 1.42 eV (the difference between the energy levels in the conduction and valence bands — call this E_g).

From Planck,

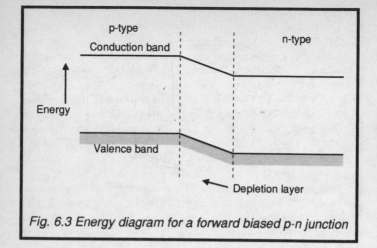

Fig. 6.3 Energy diagram for a forward biased p-n junction

$$E_g = hf \therefore f = \frac{E_g}{h} = \frac{1.42 \times 1.602 \times 10^{-19}}{6.626 \times 10^{-34}}$$

$$= 3.43 \times 10^{14} \text{ Hz},$$

or

$$\lambda = \frac{3 \times 10^8}{3.43 \times 10^{14}} = 8.75 \times 10^{-7} \text{ m} = 875 \text{ nm}$$

which as Figure 1.7 shows is just in the infra-red region. From the above therefore each time an electron combines with a hole, a photon of energy E_g is released.

This wavelength is too high for an LED to be used as a miniature indicator lamp so it is more likely that another semiconductor would be involved such as gallium arsenic phosphide (GaAsP) which has a larger energy gap of around 2.0 eV. This therefore increases the frequency of emission to say, 4.84×10^{14} Hz which as Figure 1.7 shows, produces orange coloured light. This is nearing the region at which the eye is most sensitive (see also Sect.3.2). In fact for peak eye sensitivity a photon energy of about 2.2 eV is needed, this is quite easily attainable.

LED's have many uses, here are some most commonly found:

Indicator Lamps: these are available in many shapes and sizes, e.g. the smallest at some 2 mm diameter up to the larger ones at around 10 mm. A sketch of a typical lamp is given in Figure 6.4(i). The plastic dome which protects the semiconductor head is of glass or resin and the connecting leads are of different lengths so that the device is connected into the right polarity. The forward voltage drop is of the order of 2.0 at a current range of $10 - 30$ mA. Generally a series resistor is added to limit the current to a safe level.

Seven-Segment Displays: these are numeric displays of seven LED's arranged as a figure of eight as shown in Figure 6.4(ii). These displays are everywhere on television and radio sets, video recorders, microwave cookers, calculators, clocks and the like. When two or more of the LED's are energised, any of the figures $0 - 9$ can be displayed, e.g. if elements a, b, g, c and d are illuminated, a figure 3 is displayed. The arrangement is usually driven by a special integrated circuit. Usually red LED's are employed although green and yellow are also manufactured. Although classed as a numeric display, it is clear that certain letters can also be shown.

Fibre-Optic Transmission: the emission of light when the junction is forward biased, the speed at which they can work, their small size and low power requirements make LED's very useful as optical transmitters — see Chapter 8.

6.2 Detectors

It goes without saying that the most common light detector (i.e. *photodetector* — photo from Greek *photos* = light) is the human eye, a truly remarkable device (Sect.3.2) but one capable of measurement which can only be classed as indeterminate.

Photodetectors mainly work on the techniques of converting incoming photons directly into electrons, the movement of which can be measured as an electric current. The conversion efficiency, i.e. the number of incident photons required on average to release one electron, is known as the *quantum efficiency*. This has a value of 100% if one electron

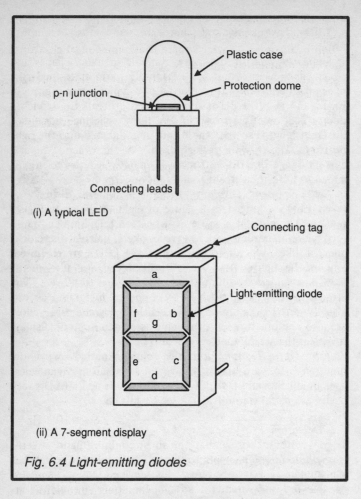

(i) A typical LED

(ii) A 7-segment display

Fig. 6.4 Light-emitting diodes

is released per incident photon. Also we must never forget that for release of an electron the energy available from an incident photon (Sect.1.3.2 and 2.2.1) must be equal to or exceed that required to raise the electron from the valence to the conduction band for the particular material (see also Fig.1.2).

Photodetectors may be classified into three separate types:

photoconductive − in which the conductivity of a material changes due to the action of light;

photoemissive − in which there is an emission of electrons from certain materials exposed to light;

photovoltaic − in which an electric current flows through the junction between two dissimilar materials exposed to light.

The application of these effects is considered below.

6.2.1 Photoconductive Devices

General terms for these are *light-dependent resistor* and *photoresistor*, the former in fact indicates the basic operation. In certain insulating and semiconducting materials incident photons may provide electrons with sufficient energy to break free of their atoms, i.e. energy-wise to move from the valence to the conduction band. The condition under which this happens is that the photon energy must be equal to or greater than the band-gap energy, E_g (see for example, Fig.5.3).

From Planck's work, the photon energy is equal to hf where h is the Planck constant (Sect.1.2.2) and f is the frequency of the radiation. Accordingly for photoconductivity to occur, hf must be equal to or greater than E_g and under this condition the material conductivity increases noticeably.

E_g for silicon is 1.1 eV and for germanium, 0.7 eV, hence photoconductivity arises in silicon for example, at frequencies at or above

$$E_g/h \text{ Hz, i.e. } \frac{1.1 \times 1.602 \times 10^{-19} \text{ J}}{6.626 \times 10^{-34} \text{ J s}} = 2.66 \times 10^{14} \text{ Hz}$$

(1128 nanometres) which is in the infra-red region. Most visible frequencies are therefore also effective. For germanium the lowest frequency is 1.7×10^{14} Hz, effective therefore at even lower infra-red frequencies.

When this condition applies, the number of charge carriers (electron-hole pairs) increases, accordingly the material resistance is reduced. If a voltage exists across the material the current therefore increases when photons of sufficient energy arrive. Note that photons of energy less than that indicated by the band-gap will not be absorbed.

The *rate* of reduction of resistance (or increase in conductance) of the material is limited by the charge-carrier lifetime because any change remains constant until the electron recombines or is removed. Response to changes in light is therefore rather slow. Thus for alternating current work such devices have a very limited bandwidth (i.e. generally not greater than 100 Hz). Bandwidths can be increased however by use of a radio frequency bias.

Two compounds which respond mainly within the visible spectrum are cadmium sulphide and cadmium selenide. Cadmium is a metal and its sulphide response is greatest at about 600 nm (orange/yellow – Fig.1.7) whereas the selenide peaks nearer the red at just over 700 nm. For a response at maximum between these two a mixture of the sulphide and selenide is used for a response at, say 660 nm. As light-sensitive resistors these are especially useful in camera exposure systems. Physically they are simple, consisting for example of no more than a thin layer of the compound on a ceramic base with printed aluminium connections. Resistance change can be high, e.g. a cadmium sulphide photoresistor may have a "dark" resistance of several megohms, falling to around 100 – 200 ohms in bright sunshine. Unfortunately the dark resistance is not constant, it can change considerably as time in the dark increases, even up to about 10 times. On the other hand changes in the "illuminated" resistance with time may be quite small. Several other materials are also used, e.g. lead sulphide which is especially useful for infra-red radiation as its main response is at 2,200 nm which is well down in the infra-red.

The simple resistance change with variation of illumination has many practical uses. Alarm systems may be operated when a beam of light normally illuminating a photoconductive device, is interrupted. On this same basis counting systems are arranged so that interruptions of a light beam (e.g. by objects on a conveyor belt) are totalled on a counter. Alternatively resistance changes may be used to indicate light level so that lighting can be switched on at dusk and off at dawn.

6.2.2 *Photoemissive Devices*

Photoemission in practice is the emission of electrons from a *photocathode* when incident photons from a beam of light are absorbed. Materials used for the cathode must have a low work function (the energy required for liberation — Sect.5.1). On entering a material a photon in colliding with an electron gives up its energy and therefore disappears. The electron is released from the surface of the material provided that the energy gained exceeds the work function of the material. Based on Planck's formula, Einstein's photoelectric equation states that the maximum kinetic energy of emitted electrons when absorbing photons of frequency f is given by:

$$E_{max} = 1/2 \, mv^2 = hf - \phi$$

where h is the Planck constant, ϕ is the work function, m is the electron mass and v its maximum velocity.

Electrons are excited from different energy states, they are obliged to move within the material to the surface and finally to overcome the surface potential barrier (the space charge — Sect.5.1). Photoemission from some metals is poor because excited electrons within the material suffer too many collisions before reaching the surface. Some metals also reflect light at the surface, hence generally insulators and semiconductors provide greater yields.

It can be shown that most photocathodes do not respond with the release of electrons with incident light at wavelengths greater than 1 μm (in the infra-red), in fact most materials in use work between about 400 and 900 nm.

A simple photoemissive device consists of an evacuated tube containing a photocathode in close proximity to an anode. The anode is maintained positive relative to the cathode and so attracts and collects the emitted electrons.

A *photomultiplier* is an extension of the photoemissive device in that it contains several additional emitters called *dynodes* as shown in Figure 6.5. Through the photoelectric effect primary electrons are emitted from the photocathode when the window is illuminated and it is these which initiate the electron cascade. The dynodes are biased at increasingly higher potentials from cathode to anode, hence free and travelling electrons are accelerated towards them at each stage (biasing circuits are not shown in the figure). On striking

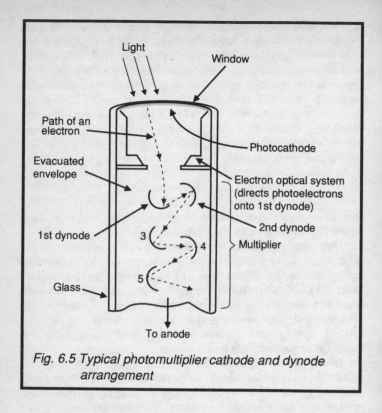

Light

Window

Path of an electron

Photocathode

Evacuated envelope

Electron optical system (directs photoelectrons onto 1st dynode)

2nd dynode

1st dynode

3

4 ⎫ Multiplier

5

Glass

To anode

Fig. 6.5 Typical photomultiplier cathode and dynode arrangement

a dynode an electron, because of its high energy causes several secondary electrons to be released, these also are attracted towards the next dynode because it is biased to a higher positive potential. As the stream progresses along the dynode chain therefore the number of electrons in it increases many times hence the anode current is considerably greater than the initial photocathode current. Materials used for the dynodes are those which have high secondary emission ratios, e.g. an alloy of the two elements, copper and beryllium.

If each dynode stage has a charge (i.e. current) amplification of σ, then for n successive dynodes, the overall amplification is given by σ^n. This can be as high as $10^8 - 10^9$ for a 10-stage multiplier. Even more stages are in use.

The progressively higher voltage required to transfer electrons from each dynode to the next is usually developed from a resistive voltage-divider network. The power supply voltage depends on the number of dynodes and in practice may have a value of one up to several kilovolts. Response times are very short, even down to 10 ns.

Photomultipliers are especially useful in *scintillation counters*. In physics scintillation is a flash of light generated within a material by the arrival of an ionizing particle. Photomultipliers are extensively used to detect single flashes of light when a scintillating material is bombarded by a single particle, usually the result of nuclear action. Each flash of light generates an insufficient number of photons for straightforward measurement, hence the use of a photomultiplier, the output of which operates a counter. From this it is also clear that the photomultiplier is an essential part of a low-level light detector — as an example, in astronomy the light from a distant star can be measured. The photomultiplier also has many applications in photometry and spectrometry (examination of radiation according to its wavelength). Sensitivity is such that even a single photon can be detected!

6.2.3 Photovoltaic Devices

These are based on the fact that when a junction between two opposite polarity semcionductors or a junction between two dissimilar materials is exposed to electromagnetic radiation, a voltage appears across the junction. In more detail and considering a simple p-n junction, absorption of incoming photons at the junction can provide sufficient energy for exciting electrons from the valence into the conduction energy band. Concurrently therefore holes must develop in the valence band. This is always with the proviso that the energy of each photon exceeds that of the band-gap (see Fig.5.3). Hence for each successful incoming photon an open-circuit voltage is produced and if there is a load resistor, a current will flow. The current is proportional linearly to the incoming photon energy.

P-N Junction Photodiode — we consider the photodiode first because the phototransistor is simply a development of it. These are active devices. In a way a photodiode is similar to an ordinary semiconductor diode except that there is a transparent area on the outer case through which light can penetrate and reach the junction. Silicon photodiodes for example are constructed from a thin wafer of n-type material which has a p-type layer diffused into it to a depth of the order of 1 μm. In use the junction is reverse-biased as shown in Figure 6.6(i), i.e. negative to p, positive to n. Electrons in the n-type material are attracted towards the positive battery terminal and similarly holes in the p-type flow towards the negative terminal. This cannot give rise to a continuous current however

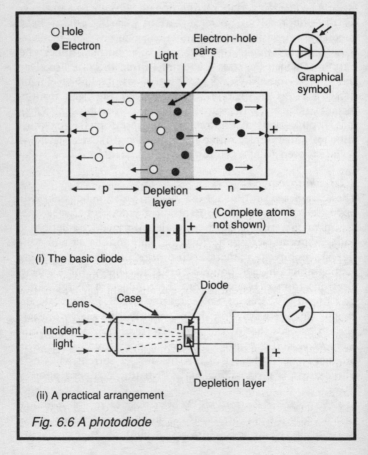

Fig. 6.6 A photodiode

because the depletion layer soon loses its majority carriers.

With no light falling on the diode, the depletion layer is therefore devoid of mobile carriers (electrons and holes) and so acts almost as an insulator between p and n. However when photons of sufficient energy enter the depletion layer, they are absorbed and their energies are released to atoms the electrons of which now gain sufficient energy for escape. The result is that the depletion layer now contains electron-hole pairs as shown in the figure. The electric field separates the electrons from the holes and although recombination takes place continually, ample charge carriers remain free and are set in motion, i.e. a current flows. A practical arrangement is illustrated in (ii) of the figure. As shown, the lens focuses the light onto the depletion layer.

We recall that the energy of a photon is given by hf where h is the Planck constant and f is the radiation frequency. Hence for silicon with an energy band-gap (Fig.1.2) of 1.1 eV, photons to be effective must themselves have energies of at least this value, i.e. as shown in Section 6.2.1, $f = 2.66 \times 10^{14}$ Hz or 1128 nm. This as Figure 1.7 shows is well down in the infra-red. Light of a longer wavelength (i.e. further down in the infra-red) will not therefore have sufficient energy to operate a silicon diode as a photodiode. Generally the maximum response is around 800 nm with output still usable as far as 600 nm (orange/yellow). Small-area diodes may have cut-off frequencies in excess of 1 GHz with response times a small fraction of one microsecond.

Phototransistors – may be considered as photodiodes containing their own amplifiers. The construction is such that by use of a transparent encapsulation, light can reach the base-collector junction. This junction acts as a photodiode. Usually however there is either no connection to the base or a high value resistor is connected between base and emitter. Accordingly the phototransistor operates as a two-terminal component.

With no light, the current in the collector-emitter circuit is the normal common-emitter leakage current. However when light reaches the collector-base junction, provided that the photons have sufficient energy, electron-hole pairs are created in the base region. Because of this a minority carrier photocurrent flows across the junction which is reverse biased. In an n-p-n transistor, because electrons flow out of the base region and holes are attracted into it, the forward base-emitter bias is increased according to the magnitude of the photo-current. Forward bias increases the electron flow from emitter to collector so effectively the photocurrent of the collector-base diode is amplified by the current gain of the transistor. Hence greater sensitivity is available from a phototransistor than from a photodiode. On the other hand, a phototransistor is slower in action compared with the photodiode, response times are generally in milliseconds.

P-I-N Photodiode – this is an advanced type of semiconduc-tor photodiode similar to that above but with an additional layer of *intrinsic* (pure) semiconductor material (the i-region) sandwiched between the normal p and n layers. The main improvement made by adding this layer is that junction capacitance is reduced, this is especially important when fast response is required as for example with modulated light. In fact response times as low as 0.5 ns are typical.

A sketch of a p-i-n photodiode is given in Figure 6.7. The intrinsic layer is relatively wide and is of high resistance, therefore has few free charges. Accordingly most of the applied voltage appears across this region hence the electric tension within it is high. Photons reaching the i-region create electron-hole pairs. Because with reverse bias the n-region is positive, liberated electrons cross into it via the thin depletion layer. Equally holes move into the negative p-region. The net result of both electron and hole movement is an increase in reverse current.

Avalanche Photodiodes – are operated with a reverse bias near the breakdown voltage (some 100 – 200 V). Secondary emission can arise in a reverse-biased junction when current is flowing across it hence the device is known as an *avalanche photodiode* and greater gain is obtained compared with normal photodiodes because photocurrents are internally amplified by avalanche multiplication. Leakage currents are similarly affected.

Liberated photoelectrons are accelerated by the intense electric field existing across the junction and they gain sufficient energy to create new electron-hole pairs by impact

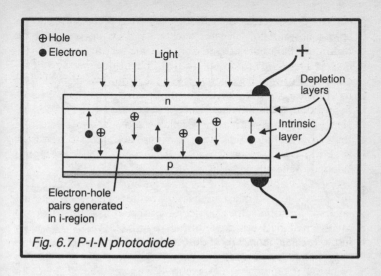

Fig. 6.7 P-I-N photodiode

ionization. This type of photodiode therefore has high sensitivity. It also has a relatively low noise performance. Material purity should be high so that plasma (Sect.6.1.3) does not form at local high voltage spots. Small area diodes such as are used for fibre-optics (Chapter 8) can respond to frequencies well into the gigahertz region.

Solar Cells — of particular interest now that satellite transmission has come to stay is the fact that at present satellites rely for their electrical power on solar-operated cells. These cells are a special form of photodiode, designed specifically for operation from radiation from the sun. Solar cells work on the same principle as for the photodiode in that electron-hole pairs are generated on the arrival of photons of sufficient energy. Although some recombination takes place continually, many of the electrons so released cross the junction into the n-region while the holes diffuse into the p-region, both under the influence of the electric field of the depletion layer. This is shown diagrammatically in Figure 6.8. Note that the n-layer is actually extremely thin to allow light to penetrate into the junction.

In a satellite for example, the output of a bank of solar cells is used to charge a secondary battery so that the satellite

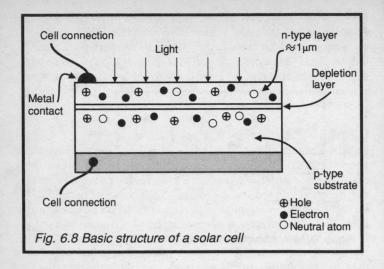

Fig. 6.8 Basic structure of a solar cell

equipment can receive a continuous and constant electrical supply irrespective of the amount of sunshine around. An earth-bound example of the use of solar cells is as a power source for telephony in isolated places where electrical power is not normally available.

Two types of cell are in general use, silicon and gallium arsenide. Generally modern silicon cells may have efficiencies up to about 15%, i.e. they convert this percentage of the incident light energy into electrical power. The output potential is some 0.5 – 0.6 V. Gallium arsenide cells operate at higher efficiencies and have a greater output voltage of about 1 V. Compared with the silicon cell however, this cell is heavier and more expensive.

Selenium Cell – the element selenium, usually found in a grey metallic form, was known firstly as a rectifier. It is a semiconductor and certain forms possess an electrical resistance which varies on exposure to light, the resistance decreasing as the intensity of the light increases. Used in this application it is therefore a photoconductive device. However selenium has also been in use as a photovoltaic element, known as a *selenium cell*. Such a cell consists of an iron base which is the positive terminal, with a very thin coating of selenium on the upper surface. This layer is in contact with a cadmium plus cadmium oxide film which is the negative terminal and which is sufficiently thin to be mainly transparent to light. Maximum response is around 570 nm (yellow/ green) and in contrast with most other photovoltaic cells, the cell potential is approximately proportional to the intensity of the light.

6.2.4 Light Pens

A light pen might be described as a hand-held photosensitive pen-shaped device generally used with a computer screen to select some part of the display for computer action and also for drawing or modifying images. Such a pen acts directly on the visual display unit of a computer and sets up a control loop from the image on the screen to the computer itself. Changes can be made to the screen image by the pen without the use of the normal keyboard. In this way a pen may be used to draw images directly on the screen. It can also be used to select from a list of choices on the screen and may also avoid repeated operations of the keyboard.

As an example of selection of a portion of a computer display, the light pen is held at the chosen spot on the screen. The computer scans the display and when the particular element in the field of view of the light pen is displayed, the pen transmits a signal to the computer for the required further processing.

6.3 Displays

The emission of light by a substance when an electric field is applied is termed *electroluminescence*. The second part of this term indicates that light is emitted by a particular substance without the addition of heat. As an example, light-emitting diodes (introduced in Sect.6.1.4) are electroluminescent. Luminescent materials which have a comparatively long decay time (i.e. after the removal of the excitation they exhibit an afterglow), are called *phosphorescent*, they may be generally known as *phosphors*. The term is related to the non-metallic element phosphorus, an extremely active material which undergoes slow combustion at normal temperatures and through this process emits light, in simple language, it glows in the dark. (Materials which have a rapid decay time are said to be *fluorescent*.) Basically light is generated within certain materials by the recombination of electrons and holes following the raising of the electrons to a higher energy level by the input of electrical energy. The excess electron energy on recombination is then relinquished in the form of a photon, i.e. light is emitted.

6.3.1 The Cathode-Ray Tube
A device well known to all based on the emission of light by a phosphorescent material is the cathode-ray tube. We normally think of these as television tubes but in fact many other types exist, e.g. in oscilloscopes for examination of electrical waveforms and for radar displays on ships and aircraft. Our interest in the cathode-ray tube is not so much in the deflection system whereby a picture or other display is built up but rather in how the phosphors on the screen are made to produce light. Figure 6.9 shows how the electron beam of a cathode-ray tube is generated and shaped. Generally tubes for oscilloscopes employ smaller screens than for television but the basic operating principles are the same.

At the end of the tube remote from the screen is the *electron gun* which might be described as a device for generating and shooting a stream of high velocity electrons from the rear to the front of the tube. The various components of the gun are shown in the figure. The tube must be evacuated to prevent interference by air molecules. It all starts with *thermionic emission* from the cathode which is kept at a high temperature by a heater inside it. Electrons which would form a space charge (Sect.5.1) are not fully restrained because the cathode is surrounded by a charged metal cylinder, the grid. The potential applied to the grid controls the electron emission by creating an electric field which aids or opposes the space charge at the cathode surface.

Thereafter the electron stream is accelerated and shaped by a chain of anodes at progressively higher positive voltages as shown in the sketch. These anodes shape the beam of electrons so that they are brought into focus on the screen. Finally at the screen, the positive voltage attracting the electrons might be of the order of 20 kV and at this voltage it

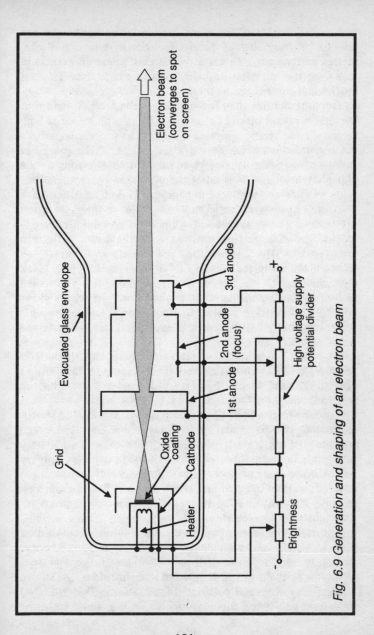

Fig. 6.9 Generation and shaping of an electron beam

can be shown that electrons arrive at the screen at the unbelievable velocity of nearly one hundred thousand kilometres *per second*. This is a special case where an extremely high electron velocity suddenly falls dramatically. There is much kinetic energy to be given up.

Our interest lies mainly with the screen for it is here that the process takes place of electrons striking a phosphor at high velocity and thereby generating light. The process is perhaps obvious from what we have discussed earlier. The energy of the electron beam is in fact transferred to electrons in the phosphor crystals. This raises the phosphor electron energies from valence to conduction band levels and so when each electron returns to the ground state (i.e. re-enters an atom orbit), light energy is released – a photon. A reminder here – we are avoiding getting involved with the beam deflection arrangements which move the spot rapidly over the screen to build up complete pictures or other images. On a black and white screen the action is relatively simple. The screen is coated on the inside with a phosphor, one which glows white on a television screen but frequently green or pale blue on a computer. Most screen glow colours can be obtained from suitable phosphors. For black and white, the beam current which is adjusted by the voltage applied to the grid (Fig.6.9) controls the brightness of the spot. A full flow of electrons in the beam therefore produces a white spot, no electrons and the screen is dark, i.e. showing black.

Colour brings added complications. As Section 3.2 shows, any colour can be made up from three primaries: red, green and blue. From this it is evident that a colour cathode-ray tube must contain three electron guns, one for each primary colour (however a more recent development works on a different system, developing three electron beams from one electron gun only). What happens is pictured in Figure 6.10. This illustrates the *shadow-mask* tube which is now in widespread use. The screen phosphor coating is more complicated than for black and white only for it comprises microscopic phosphor dots in groups of three. When any dot of a group is hit by an electron beam, it glows in its own colour. As shown in the figure, a special perforated mask ensures that electrons from each gun strike the appropriate dot, e.g. those from the

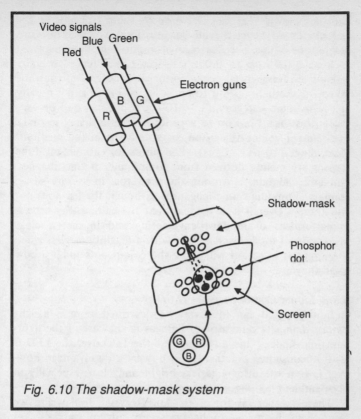

Fig. 6.10 The shadow-mask system

electron gun for red are directed only to the phosphor dots which glow red. Each phosphor dot in a group therefore contributes an amount of its colour as determined by the strength of its own electron beam (see also Sect.3.2). The figure shows a shadow mask with circular holes, a more recent development uses short vertical slots in an interlocking pattern with in-line electron guns. This system is an improvement because more electrons reach the screen instead of being intercepted and hence wasted by the mask.

Phosphor materials are highly purified crystals containing very small amounts of other elements which serve as *activators*, the purpose of which is to increase the luminescence.

Phosphors available for cathode-ray tubes are many, the efficiencies vary over a wide range, often expressed in terms of photons output per electron-volt input, values ranging from as low as 0.01 up to 0.07. Phosphor persistence generally follows an exponential decay form. It is defined as the time taken for the light output to fall to its 10% level and is usually in the medium category (1 – 100 ms) but can also be very short (less than 1 μs) up to very long (greater than 1 second). For general colour television, persistence is in the medium/short range (10 μs – 1 ms). Phosphors for cathode-ray tube screens are mainly derived from compounds of zinc, magnesium and cadmium. Among the activators in use are silver, copper, chromium and manganese although the list does not end there. Overall it is evident that the cathode-ray tube is a masterpiece of modern engineering and in fact a close inspection of a television screen with a magnifying glass when the screen is in action will show the colour dots and just how small they are.

6.3.2 Liquid Crystal Displays (LCD's)

A liquid crystal can in a way be described more as a light switch than as a generator of light as in the case of the light-emitting diode. One advantage of the LCD over the LED is that it consumes practically no power; a disadvantage however is that the display is less bright and clear, especially in poor ambient lighting.

There are several forms of liquid crystal display and we find them in many applications, e.g. digital watches and clocks, calculators, cameras, portable word processors and computers, remote control television and video recorder handsets. There are many others and surely more to follow. Several types of liquid crystals are available, however they are in fact neither fully liquid nor solid but generally exhibit properties somewhere in between.

The explanation which follows is necessarily simplified for we are dealing with a very complex subject and so we avoid considering changes in the index of refraction, phase shifts, and many other phenomena. Firstly we need to understand the meaning of the term *nematic*. A nematic liquid crystal is an organic compound in which the molecules are normally

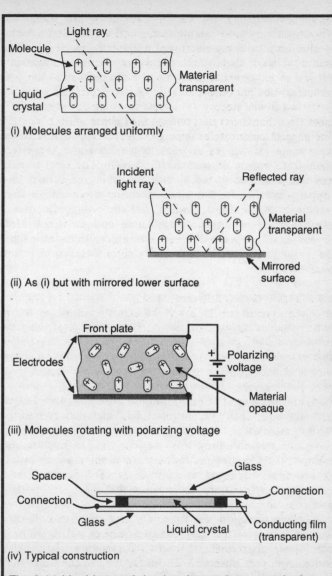

(i) Molecules arranged uniformly

(ii) As (i) but with mirrored lower surface

(iii) Molecules rotating with polarizing voltage

(iv) Typical construction

Fig. 6.11 Liquid crystals(molecules and construction)

aligned uniformly as in Figure 6.11(i). These long-chain molecules are basically elliptical in shape and are *polar*, meaning that they exhibit positive and negative poles. It is evident from the figure that all are aligned relative to a single axis (vertical in the figure and known as a *director*) and clearly as shown, rays of light can pass through the crystal between the upper and lower surfaces. In most cases the lower surface is mirrored, hence the crystal reflects the light as in (ii).

The alignment can be changed by the application of an external force such as an electric potential and the effect when this happens is considered in (iii). The electric field produces a torque on each molecule trying to turn it in a direction parallel to the electrodes, the molecules in fact become arranged in a random fashion. Accordingly the reflectivity of the liquid changes and the light is scattered, i.e. the space between the two electrodes becomes opaque. The basic construction of an LCD cell is sketched in Figure 6.11(iv).

Many such LCD units are assembled together so that (usually) numerals can be displayed in the standard 7-segment form as in Figure 6.4(ii). Such displays are not visible in the dark because they are completely reliant on the transmission of ambient light, as mentioned above, they do not generate their own light. Response time to 90% to an input voltage is somewhat slow, say 75 ms, for many applications this is no great disadvantage because this to a human being is quite a short time indeed. The decay time to 10% takes even longer, typically $100 - 150$ ms. Current for a 3-digit display is of the order of $10 \mu A$ at 5 V.

This is not the only way in which LCD's operate, for example there is the *twisted nematic* display which works by changing the polarization of light (Sect.3.3.4). As a reminder, if light is passed through a thin sheet of polarizing glass (we have sunglasses which do this), it is then polarized in a certain direction and passes through a second polarizing glass only if the latter has the same plane of polarization. In fact, if the polarizations of the two glasses are at right angles, no light will pass through. This is the basis of the *field-effect* LCD in which application of an electric field causes the crystals to act as polarizers. Consider a polarizing filter on the front of a display to control the light passing through (say, vertical polarization). If, for example the liquid crystals pass only horizontally polarized light, then the LCD is essentially switched off because no light is reflected from the back mirrored surface. Alternatively, when on application of an electric potential, the plane of polarization of the LCD is rotated to vertical, then light is transmitted to the mirror and reflected back from it.

6.4 Opto-Isolators

At last something perhaps a little easier to understand for the opto-isolator simply consists of an infra-red light-emitting diode in close proximity to a photodiode or a phototransistor, the complete assembly being contained in a light-proof encapsulation. The two components are so arranged that light from the LED actuates the photosensitive device. This therefore provides optical coupling but electrical isolation, i.e. the two circuits coupled are entirely separate electrically as shown for example for a photodiode circuit as in Figure 6.12(i). Both components are chosen so that their performances are maximum at the same light frequency (usually in the infra-red). Opto-isolators are therefore especially useful for transferring signals from one circuit to another when the two circuits have a large voltage difference between them, e.g. for safety reasons or to protect components in the lower voltage circuit from electrical breakdown.

Generally phototransistors rather than photodiodes are used with a complete circuit enclosed in a single encapsulation. Figure 6.12(ii) shows a typical phototransistor circuit. High voltage types withstand at least 7,500 volts (peak) between input and output sections. The efficiency of an opto-isolator is quoted as a *transfer ratio*. This is simply the ratio (expressed as a percentage) of the output current to the input current. Opto-isolators using photodiodes may have transfer ratios of only some 5%, with phototransistors the efficiency may be increased to 20 − 100%. Units employing special transistors may have transfer ratios exceeding 500% so indicating an output current five times greater than the input current. Frequency response is from a few kilohertz up to around 300 kHz according to type.

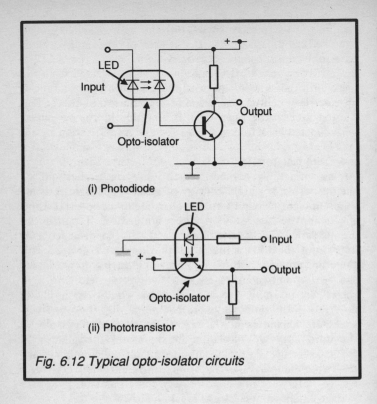

(i) Photodiode

(ii) Phototransistor

Fig. 6.12 Typical opto-isolator circuits

Chapter 7

LASERS

Perhaps here a little history will not come amiss. Not so long ago, in fact in the early 1950's the MASER was developed. The name is an acronym for Microwave Amplification by the Stimulated Emission of Radiation, in a way explaining what it is all about. A maser can produce an intense beam of microwaves with all waves in step and for example they quickly found use in amplifying very weak radio signals such as are received by radio telescopes. Then along came the LASER (Light Amplification by the Stimulated Emission of Radiation). The first working model was based on the ruby (see Sect.7.2) and was produced by Theodore H. Maiman (an American physicist) in 1960. This model produced a *coherent* red light beam of an intensity hitherto unseen.

Technically coherence may be defined as a wave property for which corresponding points on the wave front are in phase. For our purpose however we may look upon it as describing a wave of a single frequency. This is very different from the incoherent light always around us, for example sunlight is a mixture of many frequencies and most artificial lighting is similar. Maiman's laser was capable of emitting extremely short pulses of coherent light of exceptional intensity. It was a wonderful breakthrough following a period of intensive research by many scientists.

An important feature of coherent light is that it does not spread out, thus the energy in a laser beam can be so concentrated and intense that it can burn holes in a steel plate. There are gas, liquid and solid lasers.

7.1 Population Inversion

All laser activity is the result of the transfer of energy, that intangible quantity which we have defined (or perhaps only explained) as something having the capacity for doing work. Thus within the atomic world, provide an electron with sufficient energy and it can escape from its parent atom, force it to give up its new energy and it will go back home.

What we are concerned with here is that the energy given up is in the form of a photon, a tiny packet of energy of light. Within a laser this process is encouraged, it is known as *stimulated emission* and it occurs whenever a photon collides with an already excited atom.

The process is not as new as we may think, Einstein had considered it theoretically way back in 1917. Gas discharge tubes work on this principle, in them molecules are excited to high energy states and photons are emitted on return to the low energy state within some 10^{-8} seconds. The principle on which the laser operates goes one step further, it gets many more particles together in the high energy state than there are in the ground state. This is known as *population inversion* because it is not the way the atoms are normally arranged on an energy basis. The particles are then triggered to fall *en masse* to the ground state. Photons are therefore emitted as an intense flash of radiation. Let us look at this in more detail.

7.2 Stimulated Emission

With certain materials there is a *metastable* energy state (stable unless unduly disturbed) as shown in Figure 7.1(i) and atoms can remain with this level of energy for some 10^{-3} seconds before dropping to the ground state and hence emitting a photon. This change-over in energy from excited to ground level is therefore 100,000 times as long as for the normal condition.

Note that we now have three energy levels in the figure: fully excited, metastable and ground. An atom can be fully excited by providing it with the energy required to raise it from E_g to E_f when it absorbs a photon of the right frequency (Sect.2.2). It then reverts to the ground state. This is known as *spontaneous emission* but it is a continuous process with more particles at E_g than E_f. The laser goes one better in that by the technique of population inversion there can be more excited atoms than ground state ones and the change from E_f to E_g controlled. The lifetime of particles (i.e. the interval between freedom and recombination) at the upper level is long compared with that for those at the ground level. Overall therefore because the stimulated emission from atoms at the

110

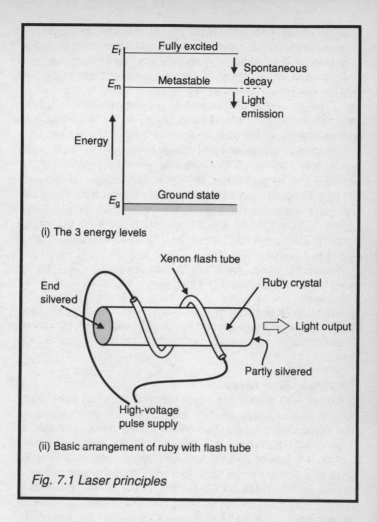

Fig. 7.1 Laser principles

In the figure:

(i) The 3 energy levels

E_f — Fully excited

Spontaneous decay

E_m — Metastable

Light emission

Energy

E_g — Ground state

(ii) Basic arrangement of ruby with flash tube

End silvered

Xenon flash tube

Ruby crystal

Light output

Partly silvered

High-voltage pulse supply

upper energy levels is greater than the absorption by atoms in the ground state, then the process results in amplification.

7.3 Lasers in Action

One of the earliest laser materials is the ruby (not the precious stone but one artifically made). A tiny percentage of chromium ions is added and this introduces the metastable condition. Population inversion in the ruby crystal is achieved by *optical pumping* which involves placing the ruby in an external light source containing photons of the required frequency for raising the atoms to the energy level E_f. Some energy is lost to adjacent atoms so some chromium ions are reduced to E_m. There is also a loss through atoms falling spontaneously the ground state.

There are many types of lasers operating on these basic principles. We recall that what is generally required is the achievement of population inversion and for this there needs to be a means of excitation. The basic material must therefore comprise atoms and molecules with energy levels which are suited to this type of application and it must have a longer particle lifetime at the upper level than at the ground level [see Fig.7.1(i)].

Generally lasers are classified according to the type of material fundamental to the operation, e.g. solid-state, semi-conductor, gas or liquid. The ruby laser described briefly above is an example of the solid-state type which as we have seen, employs materials containing a small percentage of impurity ions which can be excited to the higher energy levels.

7.3.1 Solid-State Lasers

Figure 7.1(ii) shows the basic parts of a typical ruby laser. This is one of the *solid-state* lasers. Optical pumping is via the xenon flash tube. The frequency of the xenon light is 5.44×10^{14} Hz (green — see Fig.1.7), giving a photon energy of 2.25 eV (see Sections 1.2.1 and 1.2.2) — this is the energy level of a particle when fully excited. At the metastable level the energy has fallen to 1.8 eV and this is the energy released as radiation by every chromium ion in the avalanche, resulting in an intense flash of light from the partly silvered end of the rod.

The ruby laser is in service generally. It produces powerful pulses for which there are many applications and more continue to arise. Another basic laser crystal is neodymium (Nd), an element less well known. Its ions are used in other crystals for emission in the near infra-red region, a crystal commonly employed is yttrium aluminium garnet, known generally as YAG. Such lasers work at around 1.06 μm (2.83 $\times$ 10^{14} Hz) and may be optically pumped using a xenon flash tube as for the ruby laser.

7.3.2 Gas Lasers

The first gas laser was developed a few years after Maiman's ruby laser, it appeared in 1961. In this early model a radio frequency wave is used to excite an electrical discharge in a tube containing a helium-neon gas mixture, hence producing a glow discharge. The helium atoms are excited by the radio frequency wave so creating electron collisions. These in turn pass energy to the neon atoms which therefore attain both high and low energy levels. The high energy levels are capable of producing laser action. In the laser the discharge tube is mounted between two mirrors, one fully reflecting, the other partially reflecting and through which the beam is projected. Radiation from this type of laser is in the red to infra-red. This type of laser is relatively inexpensive and widely used for example in alignment and distance measurements. The usual output wavelength is 0.633 μm (4.74 $\times$ 10^{14} Hz) which is just in the red (Fig.1.7). Outputs at 1.15 μm and 3.39 μm can also be obtained.

There are many types of gas laser in use, two most commonly found are:

(1) the argon laser with output wavelengths around 0.488 μm (green/blue) and 0.515 μm (green);

(2) the CO_2 laser which is one of the most efficient and is capable of high power output. Accordingly it is particularly useful for cutting and welding. It has outputs at several wavelengths within the range 9.6 – 10.6 μm which is well down in the infra-red.

7.3.3 Liquid Lasers

These are used to a lesser extent but they do avoid the difficulties encountered in the production of crystals required by solid-state systems. Efficiencies are comparatively low. Most commonly found is the dye laser, outputs from this type cover most of the visible spectrum down to the near infra-red.

As a single example, these lasers may be used to study energy absorption of other gases, such as exhaust emissions from vehicles.

7.3.4 Semiconductor Lasers

This type of laser relies on population inversion and generally has high efficiency in the conversion of electrical energy into light. Population inversion is usually achieved by carrier injection across a forward biased p-n junction. Absorption of photons from the external light source creates electron-hole pairs and on an energy diagram we may consider electrons to have risen into the conduction band with a corresponding number of holes in the valence band. These electrons in the conduction band are now free and can move within the lattice. Stimulated emission occurs when another incoming photon collides with a free electron forcing it to fall back energy-wise into the valence band and combine with a hole there. In so doing, by changing from conduction band to valence band the electron must reduce its energy level accordingly and so it emits a photon of the appropriate value. A sufficiently large number of electrons must first be excited into the conduction band for laser action to start up.

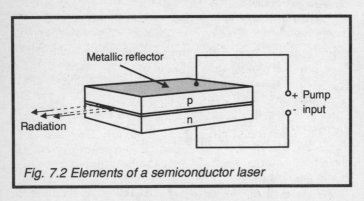

Fig. 7.2 Elements of a semiconductor laser

Figure 7.2 shows the elements of a semiconductor laser, for example one based on gallium arsenide. It is no more than a fraction of a millimetre in length. Such a device is likely to operate most efficiently between about 0.6 and 1.0 μm.

114

Contacts are formed on the upper and lower surfaces of the block. The laser is pumped by a heavy supply of electrons to the n material so that they are driven across the junction (forward bias). The figure shows a simple arrangement but in practice this is likely to be enclosed within other layers of more complex gallium arsenide compounds.

7.3.5 Conditions for Oscillation

The laser is effectively a high frequency generator comprising an optical amplifier with the necessary positive feedback to sustain oscillations. Some tuning mechanism is also required to determine the operating frequency. Here we talk in general terms simply to appreciate how a particular type of laser can produce a continuous oscillatory output.

Optical amplification occurs in the basic operation of the laser, this is how a powerful beam of light is emitted, the frequency is determined by the material used from its characteristic energy levels and transitions between them. Positive feedback may be provided by a mirror system as shown in Figure 7.1(ii). Photons generated by the laser are reflected by the silvered ends of the crystal so that they return through the medium. They are therefore available to provide further amplification. We note that oscillation only occurs in any system when the overall (or loop) gain exceeds unity, i.e. the total gains are greater than the total losses. The partly silvered end of the rod shown in the figure allows some of the light to escape which is in fact the output of the device.

If too low a voltage is applied to the laser, the total losses exceed the gain so under these conditions the laser cannot function as such. Spontaneous, but not stimulated emission occurs as shown for example in Figure 7.3. This is not true laser activity because the output is at low level and not coherent. The figure shows that as the input current is increased a point is reached where the light output increases rapidly and linearly. This change-over is at a threshold current, marked I_{th} on the figure. At this point the laser is beginning to move into the condition of oscillation, i.e. its total gains exceed the total losses. To the right of I_{th} on the figure therefore, stimulated emission is occurring, i.e. the laser is operating normally.

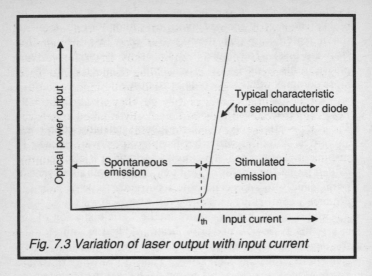

Fig. 7.3 Variation of laser output with input current

7.4 The Things They Do
Lasers and laser technology grow at an unprecedent rate. Gone are the days when we saw them as huge gun-like devices projecting a long stream of light as depicted by our film producers. Nowadays as shown in Section 7.3.4 the basic element of a laser may be no more than a fraction of one millimetre in length. It is of course impossible to list all the applications which enlist laser technology, nevertheless a few only will serve to demonstrate how powerful a tool the laser is, its versatility and that it still has enormous potential.

(1) Perhaps the first which comes to many minds is the use of a laser in optical storage, for example, reading a compact disc (CD). Digital recording is employed with more than 6×10^9 bits per disc. The digital information is impressed on the disc groove as a series of pits each a mere 0.5 μm wide. The disc is read from underneath using a laser beam so that for a digital 1 a pit reflects light onto a photodiode (Sect.6.2) whereas for a digital 0 the absence of a pit results in the reflection of considerably less light. Similar techniques are employed in television film and video recording.

(2) Fibre-optical telecommunication systems have many uses for lasers, such systems are discussed in greater detail in

(3)   The medical profession already has many uses for lasers and is continually finding new ones. An early application was the use of small pulsed ruby lasers for refixing detached retinas, in a way spot welding them back into place. Now they can even roam around inside us burning up some of our not so essential tissues as they go, they are also especially useful for the cauterization of ulcers. Even blood vessels can be sealed whereas the more powerful lasers are used for surgery, e.g. on tumours. Their functions are not limited to heating however, many other techniques such as cell counting and in heart valve operations are very successfully carried out. Overall therefore with the advent of the laser the medical profession has been able to take a leap forward in both diagnosis and cure.

(4)   The military have also embraced the laser with open arms for it now has many uses in the aiming and guidance of missiles, its coherent light output being an obvious advantage for illuminating a target. Laser rangefinders are also superior to straightforward optical systems. With their shorter wavelengths lasers have greater accuracy than radar although of course they are hopeless in fog or poor visibility. Again by using the laser's coherent light output, optical interference methods have been able to improve greatly the accuracy in measuring distance.

(5)   In industry high powered pulsed lasers are used in metalworking, e.g. for welding, cutting intricate shapes and for piercing holes, such is the energy in the beam. Because of the extremely short wavelengths involved, lasers have also found their way into copier and facsimile machines. Laser printers are used for handling high speed outputs from computers.

Above are just a few of the uses to which laser technology has been applied. Most fascinating of all perhaps is the illuminated display (seen mainly on television) in which many lasers are employed to create a hitherto unseen mêlée of criss-crossing beams of coloured light. What next?

Chapter 8

FIBRE OPTICS

Transmission of information by means of light is not necessarily new. Even way back in 1588 light from bonfires all along the Channel coast carried the message that the Spanish Armada was on its way. Thereafter optical communication was achieved by the use of beams of light, limited in range and by atmospheric conditions. A typical example is that of the Aldis signalling lamp (after its inventor, A. C. W. Aldis) used mainly by the navies and air forces for the transmission of Morse Code. Further development had to await the arrival of semiconductor optical systems and fibre optics. These have only recently been with us, in fact the first low-loss fibres (i.e. fine strands of glass carrying modulated light signals) did not arrive until the 1970's. Since then development has truly been explosive and whereas early fibres had a loss of more than 20 dB per kilometre, present day ones may have a loss of less than 0.2 dB/km and successful efforts are continuing with a view to reducing this loss still further. In fact present repeater spacings of up to 10 km are feasible, hence many routes have no repeaters at all. Fibre-optic transmission is used for both short haul purposes, e.g. within a building, or alternatively for very long distances, for example across major oceans.

The present growth of fibre-optic systems is truly phenomenal. The latest transatlantic cable (UK/US) is some 6,300 km long and for digital transmission has a data rate of 5 Gbits/s (5×10^9 bits transmitted in only one second), a transmission rate unheard of a few decades ago. Continual research will obviously increase this figure as fibres and lasers are developed further. At present it is estimated that some 60% of the world's telecommunications traffic is carried over fibres and the expectation is that this figure will increase to as much as 80–85% by the year 2000. The reasons for such expansion are perhaps obvious, however some notes follow.

The *potential* bandwidth of a fibre is as much as 30,000 – 40,000 GHz, the word potential is used because many more years will pass before this is likely to be achieved. Even 5,000 GHz is seen as feasible in the medium term. No longer will bandwidth be considered as an expensive item. Considering that coaxial cables suffer from rather high attenuations above about 1 GHz and even microwave systems are not likely to be used above about 300 GHz (usually much lower), it is clear that fibre-optic systems will continue to grow rapidly with per-channel costs tumbling. In addition their extremely small size compared with these two competitors is also greatly in their favour. This is mainly because underground ducts in which cables are laid were rapidly becoming congested with the existing metallic cables, hence the problems arising from laying more ducts in main roads have now been avoided. Fibre-optic cables are sufficiently small compared with those they replace that the existing duct system is ample. Undersea cables do not have this problem but the smaller size and flexibility of the fibre is clearly an advantage.

Figure 1.7 shows that the visible spectrum extends from about 4.1×10^{14} to 8×10^{14} Hz giving a bandwidth over the whole spectrum of 3.9×10^{14} Hz, truly a monumental bandwidth but as we might well imagine, not all of it can be used. An optical communication link is no different basically from other communication systems. Figure 8.1 shows that it

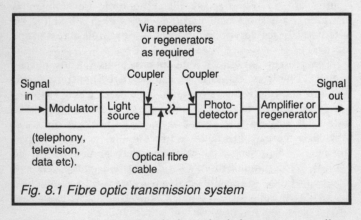

Fig. 8.1 Fibre optic transmission system

comprises a transmitter which is the light source, usually a semiconductor laser diode or light-emitting diode (LED)

120

coupled to the optical fibre channel. At the distant end the fibre is coupled to the receiver consisting of, for example a photodiode. The term *regenerator* shown in the figure refers to a device which receives digital pulses in a poor condition and transmits them onwards "as new". The two directions of transmission originally required two fibres but more recent developments now enable both to be accommodated on a single fibre. Notes on the devices mentioned are to be found in Chapters 6 and 7.

Before we consider the glass fibre as a waveguide however, it might be more advantageous to look at the basic principles of waveguides first.

8.1 Waveguides

Looking at a single optical fibre of say, a mere 100 μm diameter (somewhere around the thickness of a single human hair) does not help much in appreciation of its waveguide properties so here we first examine the heavier duty ones used at the lower frequencies such as microwaves. Electromagnetic waves can be transmitted through space and the atmosphere as is well known from broadcast and other transmissions. On the other hand the waves can be confined within metal or certain glass guides. Typically a waveguide for say, 10 − 15 GHz might be a brass rectangular tube of internal cross-sectional dimensions 2 × 1 cm with a dielectric of dry air. Over this range of frequencies the wavelengths transmitted are between 2 and 3 cm. At considerably higher frequencies, say 60 − 90 GHz (wavelengths between 0.33 and 0.5 cm), the guide internal dimensions are now reduced to 0.3 × 0.15 cm, again the longer dimension is twice that of the shorter. In a way also the dimensions are commensurate with the wavelength of the transmission.

At light frequencies therefore it might be expected that the cross-sectional dimensions of a waveguide would be extremely small and this is so, we are down to threadlike guides, the same relationship between guide dimensions and wavelength transmitted still holding.

What is important in waveguides is that because it is an electromagnetic wave which is being propagated, transmission is entirely through the dielectric and not along the walls of the guide. The wave cannot propagate axially along the guide otherwise its electric field would be continually short-circuited and therefore lost. The wave therefore progresses along the guide in a zig-zag fashion via reflections from wall to opposite wall. The principles of wave reflection are considered in Chapter 3 and are of major importance here because without total internal reflection, fibre-optic transmission as we now know it would not be here today.

As warned in Chapter 3 we may be in danger of creating the wrong impression by drawing an electromagnetic wave as a "light ray". It is certainly not as simple as that but it serves our purpose well.

8.2 The Fibre Waveguide

An unadorned single glass fibe can transmit a light wave by reflections within the fibre as illustrated in Figure 8.2(i) because glass surrounded by air satisfies the requirement $n_1 > n_2$. In this case we recall from Chapter 3 that n_1 is the index of refraction of the glass and n_2 that of the air. A difficulty with this simple technique arises however in that any lossy material supporting the fibre causes attenuation of the wave as it passes and the simple glass fibre itself may easily become scratched or otherwise damaged, again causing losses. Furthermore there would be the problem of bunching several fibres together for taking the example of just two fibres, where they lie in contact with each other the condition that n_1 is greater than n_2 no longer holds, in fact n_1 is equal to n_2 and light therefore can travel from one fibre to the other. In practice such difficulties are overcome by using a composite fibre consisting of a core of glass with a *cladding* (i.e. covering) of lower refractive index so making the fibre fully self-contained as far as the transmission of light is concerned as shown in Figure 8.2(ii).

There are two main techniques of cladding resulting in what are known as *step-index* and *graded-index* fibres as discussed below. The size of a fibre is usually denoted by two figures, the first stating the core diameter followed by the cladding diameter, both in micrometres, e.g. 50/125.

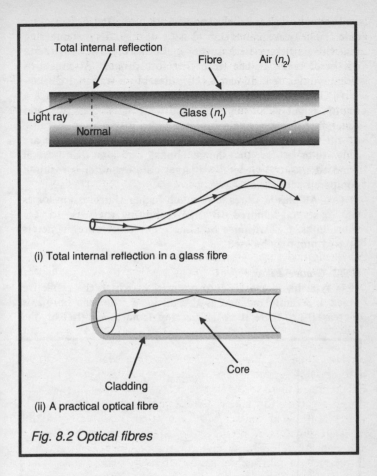

Total internal reflection

Light ray

Normal

Fibre   Air (n_2)

Glass (n_1)

(i) Total internal reflection in a glass fibre

Cladding

Core

(ii) A practical optical fibre

Fig. 8.2 Optical fibres

8.2.1 The Step-Index Fibre

For this type of fibre, progression radially from the core into the cladding is abrupt and the cladding itself has a constant refractive index throughout. Step-index fibres are available in three different forms, each conforming to the principle that the refractive index of the core exceeds that of the cladding.

(i) A glass core with a glass cladding, e.g. the core might have a refractive index of 1.45 and be enclosed within a

123

cladding of a lower refractive index of 1.43. In this particular case the critical angle is $\sin^{-1} 1.43/1.45 = 80.5°$, remembering that this is the angle a light ray makes with the *normal*. Note the small index change from core to cladding. Attenuations range from a few dB/km to considerably less than 1 dB/km.

(ii) A glass core cladded with a plastic. This requires a slightly larger index step compared with the all-glass fibre and generally this type has a somewhat higher attenuation. Because of the greater attenuation (several dB/km), these fibres are only suitable for the shorter links, e.g. less than several hundred metres. Generally a larger core diameter is required compared with the all-glass type.

(iii) All-plastic fibres have much higher transmission losses (up to several hundred dB/km) so limiting their use to very short links, e.g. within a building. For these core diameters up to 1 mm may be used.

8.2.2 *Graded-Index Fibres*
This type has a special core material in which the refractive index is steadily reduced as the distance from the fibre axis increases, i.e. there is no single step from a material of one

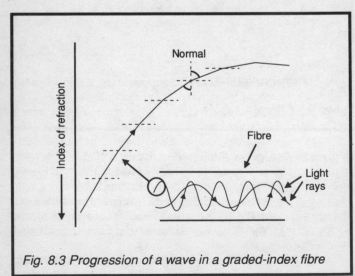

Fig. 8.3 Progression of a wave in a graded-index fibre

refractive index to another of a different index. This causes the light rays to be continually redirected towards the fibre axis, in a way they are bent over as demonstrated in Figure 8.3. In this figure we show the reduction in refractive index as a series of small steps and the angles the ray makes with the normal at each step are clearly increasing. We are reminded that Snell's Law (Chapter 3) shows that rays are bent away from the normal when travelling from a higher to a lower refractive index. Accordingly because n is decreasing as the ray progresses upwards, the ray is turned towards the horizontal, i.e. it curves over.

The figure shows the effect in all simplicity yet it is sufficient to show the continual refraction of a wave as it travels away from the centre of a graded index fibre. Ultimately total internal reflection turns it back and then, because its progression is from a lower to a higher refractive index material (n is increasing), it will be bent continually *towards* the normal until it reaches the fibre axis. Thereon the procedure repeats in the lower half of the fibre.

Not all rays can be treated as above since some on entering a fibre do not cross the axis steeply enough to be bent over whereas others are too steep to be bent over at all, these are therefore lost. Unlike the step-index fibre, the graded-index variety is normally restricted to glass.

8.3 Optical Fibre Characteristics

One of the most important characteristics of a transmission channel is its signal attenuation. Appreciable losses occur in the input coupling to the fibre and at splices but here we are concerned only with the fibre itself, the main causes of attenuation being *absorption* and *scattering*. For most optical systems the range of wavelengths usable is limited approximately to $0.5 - 1.6$ μm (i.e. $500 - 1600$ nm and as Figure 1.7 indicates, from green light down into the infra-red). Extension of the usable range both towards the ultraviolet and further into the infra-red is limited as far as glass fibres are concerned by their *intrinsic absorption*, i.e. belonging naturally to the glass itself.

Over the range quoted above we have to cope with *impurity absorption* since this mainly controls the attenuation characteristic. The importance of this can be estimated from the fact that fibres made from glass as we know it in everyday life would have unbelievably high attenuation and therefore be useless for fibre-optic transmission. Hence the normal glass impurities such as water molecules and certain metal compounds must be kept extremely low and designers talk in terms of impurity concentrations of no more than a few parts in 10^9.

Scattering is the process by which photons are deflected from their paths by density fluctuations in the core. When for example glass is molten during manufacture, the heat introduced encourages molecules to move randomly, on cooling however they are locked into position. Because this is a random process there will be variations in molecular density throughout the fibre, hence variations in refractive index. At these local density variations a ray of light passing through the fibre will experience scattering. This naturally creates a loss since some light is now projected at the incorrect angle and is therefore lost. This type of loss is known as *Rayleigh scattering* (after Lord Rayleigh, the British physicist) and it is effective only when the scattering objects have dimensions of less than one wavelength of the passing light wave. The scattering loss increases as the wavelength falls and whereas at about 2 μm the loss might be less than 0.1 dB/km, at a much shorter wavelength, say 0.5 μm, the loss may be well over 10 dB/km but of course the actual figures vary considerably with the composition of the glass.

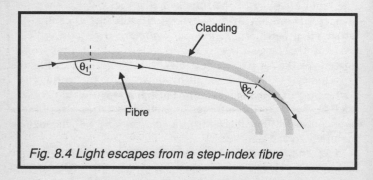

Fig. 8.4 Light escapes from a step-index fibre

A characteristic which may come into play when a fibre is curved is that of *bending loss*. How this arises is shown in Figure 8.4 in which is shown a step-index fibre. The light ray is reflected at the first point by total internal reflection because θ_1 is equal to or greater than the critical angle of reflection. However at its subsequent encounter with the cladding, it now arrives at the angle θ_2 which is less than the critical angle, hence the ray is not reflected but instead undergoes refraction through the cladding. It is refracted again on passing from the cladding into the surrounding air. Such a ray is therefore lost. Clearly the losses decrease as the bend radius increases.

8.3.1 Propagation Modes
In electromagnetic wave transmission within a waveguide (Sect.8.1) a *mode* is the form or state of oscillation of a particular wave, it in fact describes the electric and magnetic field patterns. With optical fibres of very small diameters there is only one mode possible, i.e. transmission is *monomodal*. Larger diameter fibres can support several different modes at once, these are generally classed as *meridional* for which the ray passes through the fibre axis after each reflection or *skew* which indicates rays which never intersect the axis.

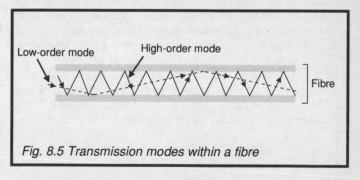

Fig. 8.5 Transmission modes within a fibre

Figure 8.5 illustrates in all simplicity the passage of high-order and low-order modes through a fibre. With the high-order modes the rays are reflected a relatively large number of times as shown, conversely low-order mode rays are reflected less frequently. Clearly the distance travelled by each mode is different and at the distant-end this is measured as *modal dispersion*.

Graded-index fibres produce less modal dispersion compared with the step-index type. With the graded-index, the refractive index is maximum at the core centre, falling steadily as the distance from the core centre increases. A high number of refractions per unit length of the fibre implies that the high-order mode rays will travel more quickly through the high refractive index centre of the fibre than the low-order modes (see Fig.8.5). By careful design of the fibre for a given wavelength range, modal dispersion can be made small.

8.3.2 Numerical Aperture

This is a measure of the ability of an optical system to accept light over a wide range of angles. We are concerned with optic fibres and from Figure 8.6(i) it is clear that not all rays arriving at a fibre end will be transmitted along the fibre. The sketch indicates that a ray entering at an angle such as that shown strikes the wall at an angle less than the critical angle, it therefore passes through both fibre and cladding into the surrounding air. Reducing the angle of entry as in (ii) enables a ray to be transmitted along the fibre because it strikes the cladding at an angle equal to or greater than the critical angle. θ_i is known as the *acceptance angle*. This is the maximum angle of incidence for which propagation into and along the fibre is possible. The *numerical aperture* which gives us an indication of the efficiency of coupling of light into a waveguide, is the sine of the acceptance angle. Accordingly a ray entering the fibre at an angle θ_i to the normal will strike the cladding at an angle θ_c, again to the normal, where θ_c is the critical angle at the point where core and cladding meet. Then:

$$\text{numberical aperture, NA} = \sin \theta_i ,$$

so that:

$$n_0 \sin \theta_i = n_1 \sin (90 - \theta_c)$$

(the two normals are at right angles to each other)

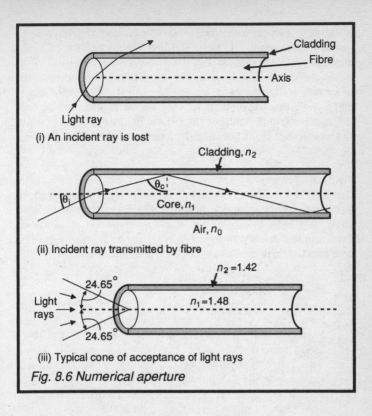

(i) An incident ray is lost

(ii) Incident ray transmitted by fibre

(iii) Typical cone of acceptance of light rays

Fig. 8.6 Numerical aperture

$\therefore$ $$n_0 \sin \theta_i = n_1 \cos \theta_c$$

and since $n_0 = 1$, it can be shown that:

$$\text{numerical aperture} \ (\sin \theta_i) = \sqrt{(n_1{}^2 - n_2{}^2)} \ .$$

An example may help to make this clear. Suppose a core has a refractive index of 1.48 with a cladding of refractive index 1.42. Then:

$$\text{numerical aperture} = \sqrt{(1.48^2 - 1.42^2)} = 0.417$$

$$\text{acceptance angle} = \sin^{-1} 0.417 = 24.65°$$

hence rays of light converging on the end of the fibre at a greater angle relative to the axial line would be lost. This is illustrated in Figure 8.6(iii).

This is now involving us rather deeply in waveguide theory so we will not probe more except to note that the sketches of light ray transmission we have used so far in this chapter are very much simplified in that they show light as single rays only whereas in fact many electromagnetic waves may be travelling together.

8.4 Light Sources

The light source or more technically the optical transmitter, is a device which accepts a modulated input current and transforms this into a light beam similarly modulated which is then coupled directly into a fibre. Some characteristics of a light source which are desirable or even essential are:

(1) the output wavelength must coincide with a region of low attenuation for the fibre to be used;

(2) an ample signal power output is required so that longer fibre lengths can be utilized before the signal power has been reduced to a level at which detection is not possible;

(3) modulation of the light output should be possible over a wide range of modulating frequencies. The output must respond rapidly to a change in input level;

(4) so that ample signal power is coupled into the fibre the light source emitting area should be small;

(5) it should be operable over the ambient temperature range likely to be encountered without excessive change in its characteristics especially in the emission wavelength;

(6) lifetime should be reasonable especially for systems carrying much traffic. Generally an m.t.b.f. (mean time between failures) of 10^5 hours for most applications may be expected;

(7) the complete device should be small although this is not essential.

Light sources which satisfy the above criteria to a high degree are the semiconductor light-emitting diode (LED) and the semiconductor laser diode (SLD).

8.4.1 Light-Emitting Diodes

The principle whereby light is emitted by certain semiconductor diodes when power is fed to them is introduced in Section 6.1.4. The general principles on which semiconductor light sources operate is that of causing electrons with conduction band energies to change suddenly to valence band energies through recombination. The permitted energy levels of a semiconductor are shown diagrammatically in Figure 1.2(ii) and we note that between the conduction and the valence bands there is a gap known as the *forbidden band*. This means what it says, i.e. that no particle can have an energy level within this band. The valence band contains complete atoms together with atoms minus one or more electrons, these we call *holes*. Because an atom (which normally is electrically neutral) on losing one of its electrons, becomes positive, then we feel justified in saying that a hole is a mobile positive charge.

Summing up — give an electron in the outer orbit of an atom a sufficient burst of energy, then it can fly out of orbit, i.e. leave the atom and become available as a minute charge carrier, that is an electric current. On Figure 1.2(ii) that electron has left the valence band and reappeared in the conduction band.

Of course it is not quite as simple as this. Although in the drawing the electrons in the conduction band seem to be separated from the atoms in the valence band, we must not lose sight of the fact that this is an *energy* diagram. All these particles are still milling around together and collisions occur with the result that free electrons with conduction band energies recombine with holes and fill them so returning atoms to their normal neutral states. But, and this is the important point, the electron must rid itself of its conduction band energy in order to recombine with a hole. In certain semiconductor materials this energy is released as optical energy in the form of a photon, i.e. there is an emission of light.

Let us move on next to Figure 1.8(ii) showing a semiconductor diode. The n-type material has a number of free electrons, therefore with conduction band energy levels [Fig.1.2(ii)] whereas the p-type has a number of free holes with valence band energy levels. Where the two types of

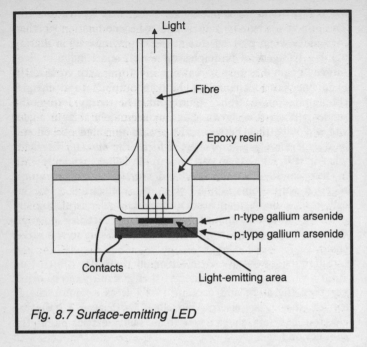

Fig. 8.7 Surface-emitting LED

material are in contact there is a *depletion layer* in which the various particles have insufficient energy to cross either way. This is with no voltage applied to the diode. Next consider the connection of a forward voltage, i.e. negative to n, positive to p. This provides sufficient driving force for free electrons and holes to move into the depletion layer and bring about recombination with the release of photons as mentioned above. The efficiency of this process is high, most of the energy released appearing as radiation.

In a nutshell therefore, considering the LED, its radiation arises from the recombination of holes with electrons, both being forced into the junction by the application of a forward bias voltage. The radiation intensity is proportional to the diode current.

Digital modulation for example switches the current supply on and off, a flash of light being produced each time the input current switches to "on". Analogue modulation is less likely to be used but needs a d.c. bias to maintain the current in the forward direction, the modulation is then applied over this bias. Practical LED's may operate at slightly less than 100 mA at a voltage between 1.2 and 1.8.

LED's for this purpose take many forms, the main difficulty being that of coupling the light output into a fibre. A few millimetres of the cladding must be removed from the end of the fibre which is then cut accurately at right angles and finely polished. Failure to obtain a highly polished end creates scattering and greatly reduces the transfer of light. Various LED constructions are used, falling generally into the *edge emitting* and *surface emitting* types, a typical surface emitting arrangement is shown in Figure 8.7. In this figure the semiconductor diode is shown as consisting solely of n- and p-type gallium arsenide (GaAs). Other materials may be used instead of or in addition according to the wavelength range and band-gap energy required, e.g. AlGaAs and InGaAs (aluminium and indium gallium arsenide).

8.4.2 Laser Diodes

To minimize continual reference back to Chapter 7 it may be advantageous to rediscover the basic laser operating principles. Energy-wise, atoms are normally in the ground state, i.e. with lowest energy. An electron in an atom which absorbs energy rises to a higher energy state and the atom is then said to be *excited*. The atom can subsequently drop back to its original energy state by radiating a photon. Such radiation is known as *spontaneous emission*. However atoms may remain sufficiently long in the higher energy state that other incoming photons can force them to emit their existing photons and therefore drop back to the ground level. If the number of atoms in the excited state exceeds that for the ground state then the condition of *population inversion* arises. Each photon on encountering an atom in the excited state causes the additional photon release to take place in such a way that the two photons are additive. This is *stimulated emission*, a feature of lasers but not LED's which emit light by spontaneous emission only. Because the emitted photons are travelling within the region where stimulated emission is possible, there is amplification. A laser is therefore a light generator operating at a very high frequency provided that sufficient positive feedback is applied. This for example can be arranged by use of mirrors as suggested in Figure 7.1(ii) and it is clear that the optical gain of the system is a function of the reflectivities of the two mirrors (reflectivity is the ratio of the reflected to the incident power).

Figure 7.3 shows a typical optical power output/input current characteristic for a semiconductor laser diode. Input current at I_{th} for most lasers is of the order of milliamperes, seldom exceeding 250 mA, usually much less. Applied voltages range between 1 and 2. For fibre-optic communications it is essential that the laser can be turned on and off at very high rates indeed.

Modulation of a semiconductor laser diode is usually effected by variation of the drive (input) current. Analogue modulation naturally requires an output which is strictly linear with the input signal and it may be that this factor limits the range of a laser diode for this purpose. On the other hand, digital modulation is more tolerant of non-linearity and so may be more easily handled. With these diodes I_{th} increases with temperature and causes a shift in the emission wavelength, accordingly special circuit arrangements may be built in to regulate the current even though heat sinks and other cooling are provided. Modulation is discussed in greater detail in the next section.

8.5 Modulation

We ought first to remind ourselves as to the essential features of the two very different types of modulation in use. Modulation is the process by which certain characteristics of a *carrier wave* are modified in accordance with the characteristics of another wave, known as the *modulating wave*. Here the ultimate carrier wave is at some frequency of light, i.e. above 10^{14} Hz. On its own a carrier wave carries no information except that it is either on or off. When modulated however information is carried and generally a carrier wave frequency must be several times the maximum modulating wave frequency. From this it follows that the higher the carrier frequency, the greater is its potential to transmit a wide band, hence fibre-optic channels are able to carry truly enormous quantities of information.

We are concerned with the two main methods of modulating the outputs of LED's and lasers, analogue and digital. The analogue signal is one which has a similarity with the original quantity it represents. A digital signal is completely different, it is effectively a means of carrying information by a series of pulses which have two values only, generally referred to as 0 and 1.

Speech and music are both analogue and may be transmitted as such, they can also be transformed into a digital form before being transmitted. Then at the receiving end of a communication channel the digital is converted back into its original analogue form. Computers and the like work in digital which is transmitted directly, there is little requirement for changing to analogue.

Briefly, when analogue information is to be transmitted over a digital system it must first be *sampled*, meaning that the amplitude of the analogue signal is measured at certain regular time intervals. Sampling need only be at the rate of just over twice the maximum analogue frequency, for example, telephony speech circuits having a maximum frequency of 3.4 kHz are sampled at 8 kHz. The voltage of each sample indicates the amplitude of the waveform at the particular instant of sampling. This amplitude measurement is then transmitted as a digital code which is simply a series of pulses interspersed with spaces.

Because digital transmission consists of a series of pulses, for long circuits it has the advantage of being able to use *regenerators* which are devices capable of accepting a relatively poor digital signal and transmitting onwards a signal identical with the original. This contrasts with analogue transmission where line amplifiers have no choice but to amplify noise and distortions picked up by the signal on its way. After several amplification stages therefore an analogue signal may be quite different from the original but the digital is "as new". A digital transmission system therefore provides a transmission quality independent of distance. We will find that digital transmission is ideally suited to the requirements of optical fibres.

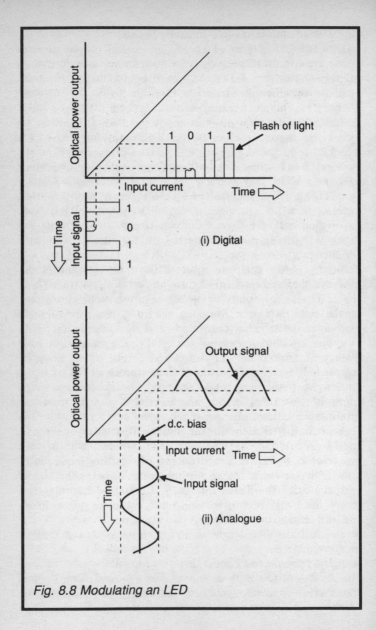

Fig. 8.8 Modulating an LED

8.5.1 Modulation of Light-Emitting Diodes

The LED is a device which has an optical output directly proportional to the forward driving current as indicated in Figure 8.8 which shows the operating conditions for both digital and analogue inputs. Emission is in the infra-red (Fig.1.7). Digital is considered first because it is more easily understood since no bias current is required. Clearly as (i) shows, an incoming pulse (a digital 1) simply turns the LED 'on', at cessation of the pulse the device returns to 'off', the optical output power therefore follows the input current linearly. For an incoming digital 0 theoretically nothing happens, however there may be a small input current as shown especially if the digit has arrived over a communication channel. Generally we find that a 0 is seldom a pure 0, there is invariably some noise breaking through.

For an analogue input there is the added complication of a need for a d.c. bias to maintain the input current in the forward direction at all times. As shown in (ii) of the figure, this is clearly necessary otherwise negative excursions of the input signal would produce no output hence the complete signal would be greatly distorted or at the extreme, rectified. We are considering extremely high frequencies so any LED junction capacitance will reduce the output by its shunting effect. The carrier lifetime (τ) is also important, this is the mean time between a charge (electron or hole) being generated and its subsequent recombination. It is essential that the modulating current changes slowly when compared with τ. It can be shown that the optical power output is inversely proportional to $\sqrt{(1 + \omega^2\tau^2)}$ where $\omega = 2\pi f$. Hence for a given value of τ, the optic power output falls as the frequency of the input increases. As an example, when $\omega = 1/\tau$ the optical power output is reduced to $1/\sqrt{2}$ (= 0.707). This of course is for the LED only, in the design of a complete system many other losses must also be taken into account.

Modulation bandwidth for an LED is up to some 300 MHz.

8.5.2 Modulation of Lasers

Unlike the LED a laser does not have an optical output which is directly proportional to the forward driving current. On the other hand a laser diode operates much more quickly than

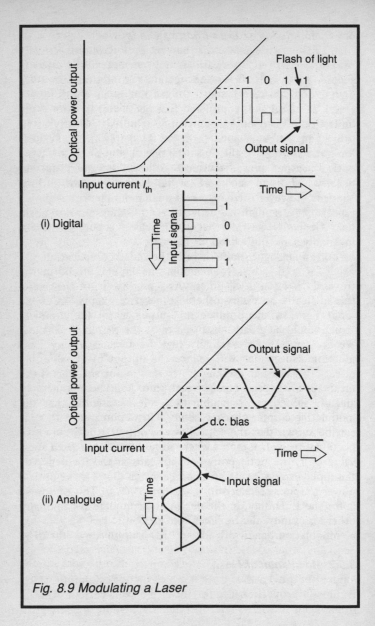

Fig. 8.9 Modulating a Laser

138

does an LED. A typical characteristic is shown in Figure 7.3. Below I_{th} increasing the input current produces only a small increase in laser output. This is due to spontaneous emission and the light output is not coherent. From I_{th} onwards however the graph shows that only a small increase in input current is required to produce a large increase in optical power output. Figure 8.9 shows the operating conditions for both digital and analogue inputs and comparison with Figure 8.8 shows that the main difference for digital modulation is simply that the laser is biased so that the input signal operates from I_{th} or just above so that the non-coherent section of the characteristic is not used.

For analogue modulation similar conditions apply, i.e. to minimize distortion a d.c. bias is applied to the laser so that negative swings of the input signal do not drive the laser down to I_{th}. Accordingly because only the straight part of the characteristic is used, the output signal is produced with little harmonic distortion (harmonics we recall are produced when a signal is distorted). Because of the fast operating speed of a laser (rise times generally less than 1ns), analogue modulation is possible up to 5GHz or even more.

8.6 Detectors

At the distant end of any fibre-optic system the signal must be *detected* meaning that it is extracted from the pulses or analogue waveforms being received see Figure 8.1. Detectors generally are considered in Section 6.2, those of most concern to us here are the semiconductor photodiodes, although other types are also in use. Silicon photodiodes have the advantage of small size, they are also relatively inexpensive. Their sensitivities are also high, operating times are short and the supply voltage required is low. However for fibre-optic systems working at a high rate the ordinary p-n diodes are generally unsuitable because their rise times (the time interval during which the leading edge of the pulse rises from 10% to 90% of the maximum pulse height) are of the order of microseconds whereas usually nanoseconds are required. Rise time is of course important otherwise action initiated by an incoming pulse is not completed by the time the next pulse arrives.

The more advanced PIN photodiode is probably the most commonly found in fibre-optic systems. The speed at which this diode operates and its overall efficiency make it a better choice compared with the normal silicon photodiode. We have already established that for an electron-hole pair to be created, an incoming photon must provide an electron with sufficient energy to raise it across the forbidden band into the conduction band (Fig.1.2). From Section 6.1.4, since $\lambda = 3 \times 10^8/f$ and from Planck, $f = E_g/h$ where E_g is the energy required for an electron to cross the forbidden energy band, then:

$$\lambda = \frac{(3 \times 10^8) \times (6.626 \times 10^{-34})}{E_g \times 1.602 \times 10^{-19}} \text{ metres}$$

$$= \frac{1.24 \times 10^{-6}}{E_g} \text{ metres} = \frac{1.24}{E_g} \ \mu m,$$

when E_g is in electron-volts. From this we can calculate the cut-off wavelength for a given semiconductor material. As an example, germanium has a forbidden band (band-gap) of 0.7 eV, hence the cut-off wavelength is $1.24/E_g = 1.77 \ \mu m$.

Similar calculations for silicon (band-gap energy = 1.1 eV) shows the lowest practical wavelength to be 1.13 μm. Both germanium and silicon responses are down in the infra-red (Fig.1.7). A typical response/wavelength characteristic for a silicon PIN photodiode is given in Figure 8.10. This indicates the cut-off wavelength and the response below (i.e. at higher frequencies).

Clearly the choice of a detector semiconducting device cannot be made without reference to the light source at the sending end of a circuit.

Avalanche photodiodes are also introduced in Section 6.2.3, they too are used as fibre-optic detectors. They are usually constructed from the same basic materials as for p-n diodes but are more complicated since they include an extra layer. They have excellent linearity (electrical power output/optical power input) over a wide range of input levels. Whereas the *responsivity* (ratio between the detector output current

140

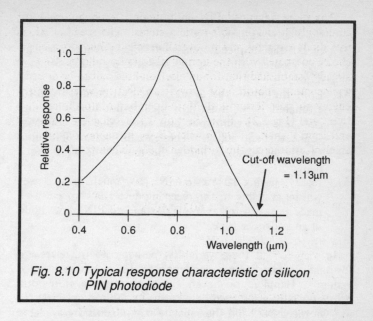

Fig. 8.10 Typical response characteristic of silicon PIN photodiode

and the optical power input) of a normal PIN diode is between say, 0.5 and 0.7 amperes per watt, that of the avalanche diode is likely to be many times greater. Avalanche diodes are therefore more likely to be used when the received signal is low over a longer than average fibre link. However they are usually more expensive.

8.7 System Design
From the several but rather brief discussions so far in this chapter, it is clear that design of a fibre-optic system involves many components. Figure 8.1 looks harmless enough but:

(1)   the frequency range of the input signal, its power levels and input noise levels have a general influence over the whole system, then

(2)   for a long-distance system the most expensive component is the fibre itself, glass or plastic. The type must then be chosen, step index or graded index. For a

shorter length system however fibre costs may not be the overriding factor;

(3) to suit the frequency range and fibre system chosen, the light source can now be planned, e.g. LED or laser diode;

(4) from the above the overall system attenuation can be estimated. This must now include not only fibre loss and repeater gains but also losses due to couplers, connectors and splices. These are difficult to determine exactly in advance, hence the use of the word "estimated";

(5) finally, having now estimated how much optic power will be available to the receiving device, a choice can be made between for example, a standard PIN photodiode or an avalanche type.

In view of all these variables, perhaps we ourselves are fortunate in *not* being called upon to design a long-distance system. Happily too, even the short-distance fibre-optic systems available for home use have all of this worked out for us. On the other hand the separate components are available so there is nothing to stop us trying.

Appendix 1

REMINDERS

Assailed as we are by information thrown at us from so many different sources, we may be forgiven for lapses of memory especially those concerning the classification of electronic quantities. Some help is given below.

A1.1 Scientific Notation

Our difficulties arise mainly from the fact that in electronics we may encounter both very large and also very small numbers. Writing them in the normal way using many noughts makes the arithmetic unwieldy and the number of noughts has to be counted, hence the probability of error. With scientific notation we write numbers in a kind of shorthand and the following examples are sufficient to explain the system:

1,000 in scientific notation is written 1×10^3
or simply 10^3

1,000,000 in scientific notation is written 1×10^6
or simply 10^6

i.e., 1,000,000 is the result of 1 multiplied by 10, 6 times. Equally giving a negative sign to the exponent is equivalent to division by 10, e.g. 0.000,001 is represented by 10^{-6}. All this has been done by shifting the decimal point and using the exponent to indicate the number of shifts. A positive exponent indicates a decimal point shift to the left, a negative exponent indicates a shift to the right.

No problems with numbers such as these but approximations may arise when mixed numbers are involved. As an example, the mass of an electron may be quoted as 9.1095×10^{-31} kilograms, clearly it is considered that the inaccuracy created by the omission of any figures which follow the 5 can be tolerated. In fact a value of 9.1×10^{-31} is frequently used.

Note that the figures are usually *normalized*, meaning that only one digit precedes the decimal point, e.g. 9.1095×10^{-31} is preferable to 91.095×10^{-30}.

A1.2 The International Unit System (SI)

Brief explanations and/or definitions are given below concerning the SI and associated units used in the main text:

AMPERE (A): is the SI unit of current and it is that constant current which, maintained in two straight parallel conductors of infinite length, 1 mm apart, produces between the conductors a force of 2×10^{-7} newtons per metre of length.

CANDELA (cd): is the unit of luminous intensity. It is defined in the SI system as the luminous intensity, in the perpendicular direction, of a surface of $1/600,000$ m^2 of a black body at a temperature of freezing platinum under a pressure of 101,325 newtons per square metre.

COULOMB (C): the charge transported in one second by a constant current of one ampere, i.e. charge $(Q) = I \times t$ coulombs (C) where I is the current in amperes and t is the time in seconds. (Named after Charles Augustin de Coulomb, the French engineer and physicist).

FARAD (F): is the unit of capacitance (named after Michael Faraday). It is the capacitance of a capacitor between the plates of which there appears a difference of potential of one volt when it is charged by a quantity of electricity equal to one coulomb. It is an inconveniently large unit so we usually work in sub-multiples, e.g. microfarad (10^{-6} F), nanofarad (10^{-9} F) and picofarad (10^{-12} F).

HENRY (H): (after Joseph Henry, the American physicist). This is the unit of self and mutual inductance and permeance. A circuit has an inductance of one henry if an e.m.f. of one volt is induced in it when the current is changing at the rate of one ampere per second.

HERTZ (Hz): the unit of frequency named after Heinrich Hertz, the German physicist. It is simply the number of cycles through which a wave or vibrating body moves per second.

JOULE (J): the unit of energy, work and quantity of heat. In electronics the following definitions apply:
 (i) it is the work done when a charge of one coulomb is moved through a difference in potential of one volt;
 (ii) it is the work done when one ampere flows through a resistance of one ohm for one second;
 (iii) it is the energy produced when a power of one watt is dissipated in one second.
(The joule is named after James Prescott Joule, the English scientist.)

KILOGRAM (kg): is the mass of an international prototype which is a block of platinum held at the International Bureau of Weights and Measures at Sèvres (a suburb of Paris).

LUMEN (lm): is the luminous flux per unit solid angle from a uniform source of one candela.

METRE (m): is the unit of measurement of length. It was originally defined based on physical phenomena, i.e. one ten-millionth of the distance from the North Pole to the Equator. It is now more precisely defined as 1,650,763.73 wavelengths of the orange light emitted by a certain isotope of the gas krypton.

NEWTON (N): is the SI unit of force. It is that force which when applied to a mass of one kilogram gives it an acceleration of one metre per second per second (m/s^2).

PERMEABILITY: is not itself an SI unit but is derived from the SI. It is a measure of the ease by which a material is magnetized, i.e. a measure of the magnetic flux set up in a substance when a magnetic field is applied. Permeability is designated by μ and it is the ratio of the flux density B and the magnetic field strength H producing it, i.e. $\mu = B/H$ henrys per metre (H/m).

The *permeability of free space* or *magnetic constant* is that of a vacuum and is given the symbol μ_0 of value $4\pi \times 10^{-7}$ henrys per metre.

Relative permeability (μ_r) is a more practical unit and is the amount by which the magnetic flux density is increased or decreased when a particular material is substituted for free space. Hence $\mu = \mu_r \times \mu_0$. Relative permeabilities range from a little less than 1 up to many thousands.

PERMITTIVITY: is not itself an SI unit but is derived from the SI. It is a measure of the ability of a material to store electrical energy. It is designated by ϵ and relates to the electric flux developed (as measured by the flux density, D) by a given electric field strength, E. Hence:

$$\epsilon = D/E \text{ farads per metre (F/m)}$$

The unit for D is coulombs/metre^2 and that for E is volts/metre hence the unit for D/E becomes coulombs per volt per metre, i.e. farads per metre.

The *permittivity of free space* or *electric constant* is that of a vacuum and is given the symbol ϵ_0 of value 8.854×10^{-12} farads per metre.

Relative permittivity or *dielectric constant* is a more practical unit. It is the ratio between the electric displacement in a medium and the electric displacement in free space given the same value of electric field strength. The symbol is ϵ_r and in more practical terms it may refer to the amount by which the capacitance of a capacitor is increased when a particular material is substituted for free space. Generally the value of ϵ_r is greater than unity, hence for a given voltage applied between the plates of a capacitor, the electric flux in the dielectric is greater than for air, i.e. the capacitance is higher.

The above three definitions are linked by $\epsilon = \epsilon_r \epsilon_0$.

SECOND (s): is the SI unit of time. It is defined in terms of the duration of a certain number of periods of the radiation corresponding to the transition between two stated levels of a caesium 133 atom.

STERADIAN (sr): the solid angle which, having its vertex at the centre of a sphere, cuts off an area at the surface of the sphere equal to that of a square with sides equal to the radius.

VOLT (V): is the difference of potential between two points on a conductor when the current flowing is one ampere and the power dissipated is one watt (after Alessandro Volta, the Italian physicist).

WATT (W): is the rate of working or power developed when one joule of energy is dissipated in one second. In an electric circuit this corresponds to the product of one volt and one ampere (after James Watt, the Scottish engineer).

A1.3 Multiples and Sub-Multiples of Units

Multiplication Factor	Prefix	Symbol
10^{12}	tera	T
10^9	giga	G
10^6	mega	M
10^3	kilo	k
10^2	hecto	h
10^1	deca	da
10^{-1}	deci	d
10^{-2}	centi	c
10^{-3}	milli	m
10^{-6}	micro	μ
10^{-9}	nano	n
10^{-12}	pico	p
10^{-15}	femto	f
10^{-18}	atto	a

Whereas electromagnetic waves are discussed mainly in terms of their frequencies, by continuing to do so for the optical range involves us in inordinately large numbers. Generally scientists prefer to describe such waves in terms of their wavelengths which although now giving rise to extremely small numbers, can perhaps more conveniently be described.

147

Generally used are either *micrometres* (10^{-6} m) or *nanometres* (10^{-9} m).

A1.4 Physical Constants

Quantity	Symbol	Numerical Value	Unit
Electron charge	$-e$	1.6022×10^{-19}	C
Electron rest mass	m_e	9.1095×10^{-31}	kg
Free space:			
electric constant	e_0	8.8542×10^{-12}	F/m
intrinsic impedance	Z_0	376.7	Ω
magnetic constant	μ_0	$4\pi \times 10^{-7}$	H/m
speed of electro-magnetic waves	c	2.9979×10^8	m/s
Planck constant	h	6.6262×10^{-34}	J s

A1.5 Trigonometry – Sum of Two Cosines
From the general compound angle formulae:

$$\cos (A + B) = \cos A \cos B - \sin A \sin B$$

$$\cos (A - B) = \cos A \cos B + \sin A \sin B$$

Adding the two equations together:

$$\cos (A + B) + \cos (A - B) = 2 \cos A \cos B .$$

Let $A + B = P$ and $A - B = Q$. Then:

$$A = \frac{P + Q}{2} \quad \text{and} \quad B = \frac{P - Q}{2}$$

hence:
$$\cos P + \cos Q = 2 \cos \frac{P + Q}{2} . \cos \frac{P - Q}{2} .$$

148

Appendix 2

TRANSMISSION LOSS AND GAIN

Transmission loss or gain in a system is measured most conveniently in the decibel notation. This uses logarithmic units to express power, current or voltage ratios and has two distinct advantages: (i) large numbers are reduced and so become more manageable, and (ii) in a complex system with a large number of components, each contributing a gain or a loss, calculation of the overall power etc. ratio by multiplying fractions is unwieldy. By expressing each ratio in a logarithmic unit, addition takes the place of multiplication.

The basic unit is the Bel (after Alexander Graham Bell, the Scottish-American inventor) and the number of bels transmission loss or gain is equal to the logarithm to the base 10 of the power ratio of the system (i.e. power out divided by power in). The decibel is one-tenth of one bel and is a unit of more convenient magnitude for general work. It is defined as follows:

If P_1 and P_2 are the input and output powers respectively of a system,

$$\text{Number of decibels } (n) = 10 \log P_2/P_1$$

Similarly when we are dealing with current or voltage and where Z is the impedance:

$$n = 10 \log \frac{I_2{}^2 \times Z}{I_1{}^2 \times Z} = 20 \log \frac{I_2}{I_1} \quad \text{dB}$$

or with voltage,

$$n = 20 \log \frac{V_2}{V_1} \quad \text{dB},$$

but note that both currents and voltages must be measured in the same impedances. Note however that we often deliberately go astray when calculating the voltage gain of an amplifier by using the above formula while ignoring the difference between the input and output amplifier impedances. There is no problem if we realize what we are doing and tell others.

A positive sign is used to express gain in a system, a negative sign indicates a loss. If for example, P_2 is greater than P_1, there is amplification and n is positive. Conversely, if P_1 is the greater, there is a loss and n is negative. Suppose $P_1 = 1$ mW and $P_2 = 0.5$ mW, obviously there is a power loss so n should work out to be negative. Then attenuation in decibels:

$$n = 10 \log (P_2/P_1) = 10 \log 0.5 = 10(-0.3010) = -3.01.$$

Absolute values can be quoted in decibel notation provided that a *reference* or *zero* level is known. As an example, the reference level of a quantity such as signal power is chosen and this is given the decibel value of 0. This reference level is usually indicated by an added letter to the symbol. One commonly used in electronics is the milliwatt for which the symbol now becomes dBm. Thus a power level of 100 mW may be expressed as +20 dBm because a power gain of 20 dB on one milliwatt results in 100 mW. Similarly −30 dBm is the same as 1 μW. Another commonly used reference level is one volt for which the symbol used is dBV.

Some power ratios and their equivalents in decibels are:

Power Ratio	dB
0.001	−30
0.01	−20
0.1	−10
0.25	−6 *
0.5	−3 *
1.0	0
1.25	1.0 *
2	3.0 *
4	6.0 *
10	10
100	20
1000	30

* slightly inaccurate but frequently used as a guide

150

Appendix 3

PHASE AND PHASE ANGLES

Phase may be described as a particular point on a waveform relative to a known fixed point which is usually at zero voltage or current, when the wave is moving in a positive direction. One complete cycle of a wave is said to move over 360° or 2π radians, the phase is therefore usually quoted as a fraction of either.

If two waves of the same frequency start together from the same point and both are at the same point in the cycle, they will always remain in step with each other and are said to be *in phase*. On the other hand if they start at different times so that the crest (or trough) of one wave does not coincide with that of the other, the waves are said to be *out of phase* and by an amount known as the *phase difference*. This is illustrated in Figure A3.1 which shows two waves A and B of the same frequency but with a phase difference of 60° (1.047 radians). Wave B has a phase angle relative to A of 60°, that is, B reaches any particular stage (say, zero or

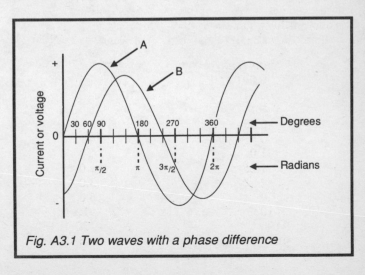

Fig. A3.1 Two waves with a phase difference

maximum) when the waves have turned through a further 60°. Knowing the frequency, the actual time delay can be calculated from:

$$t = \frac{\text{phase angle in degrees}}{360 \times f} \quad \text{or} \quad t = \frac{\text{phase angle in radians}}{\omega}$$

In the figure B is said to be *lagging* on A by 60° or equally A is *leading* B by 60°. Quite correctly, B is leading on the second cycle of A by 300°.

Note that a constant phase difference can only apply when the two waves have the same frequency, for if they have not, the phase difference continually changes. The figure also shows that the two waves may have different *amplitudes*, that is, their maximum values are different. Amplitude in no way affects phase difference.

Appendix 4

COMPLEX NUMBERS

This is a brief and incomplete look at *complex notation*, nevertheless sufficient to acquaint those who have no experience of the method at all with the basic idea. In Section 3.3.7 mention is made of the index of refraction having both *real* and *imaginary* parts. The exact meaning of the second term may escape us at first but it has arisen from the difficulty early mathematicians had in expressing the root of a negative quantity, e.g. $x^2 = -1$ has no normal solution. This problem shows itself in ordinary algebra when solving certain quadratic equations, an example being $x^2 - 4x + 13$, the solution for which is $x = 2 +/- \sqrt{-9}$. To get an answer an *operator* was invented which when squared was equal to -1 and in electrical engineering we label the operator "j", hence

$$j3 \times j3 = j^2 9 = -9 \text{ hence } \sqrt{-9} = j3 \text{ (since } j^2 = -1)$$

In early days there was confusion over this breakdown of reality so these numbers were called "imaginary" and quantities with both real and imaginary parts were said to be "complex", hence the system is generally known as Complex Notation or Complex Algebra. In electrical engineering we find the system ideal for handling phase differences in a.c. networks mathematically.

The four quadrants around real and imaginary axes are illustrated in Figure A4.1(i). The 3 o'clock axis is taken as the reference and rotation is anti-clockwise. It is a *real* axis. At 90° is the *imaginary* axis labelled j so we can perhaps define j as an operator which rotates an axis by 90° anti-clockwise. On this basis a further multiplication by j brings us to the real axis again, hence by rotating 90° from the imaginary axis gives $j \times j = j^2 = -1$, a real axis but moving negatively. A further multiplication by j brings us again to the imaginary axis below the real axis where we have $-1 \times j = -j$.

153

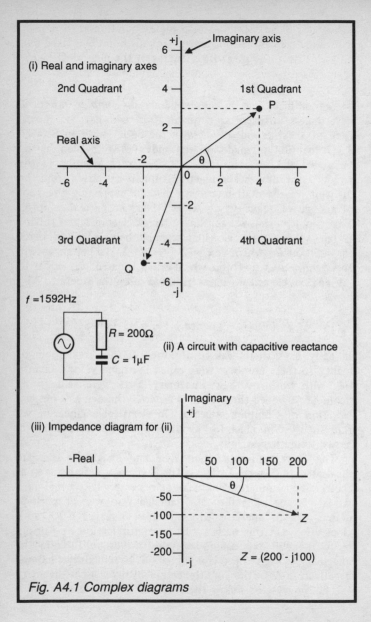

(i) Real and imaginary axes

+j
Imaginary axis

2nd Quadrant

1st Quadrant
P

Real axis

θ

3rd Quadrant

4th Quadrant

Q

$f = 1592Hz$

$R = 200\Omega$

$C = 1\mu F$

(ii) A circuit with capacitive reactance

(iii) Impedance diagram for (ii)

Imaginary
+j

-Real

θ

Z

$Z = (200 - j100)$

Fig. A4.1 Complex diagrams

154

Point P can be expressed in complex notation as $(4 + j3)$, the 4 is real and the 3 imaginary. Equally point Q is fixed by $(-2 - j5)$ or $-(2 + j5)$. The lengths of the phasors OP and OQ are easily calculated from their complex numbers for:

$$OP = \sqrt{(4^2 + 3^2)} = 5 \qquad OQ = \sqrt{(2^2 + 5^2)} = 5.4$$

These are lengths only, the phasor positions in the quadrant are revealed by the angles made with the real axis for:

$$\tan \theta = \frac{\text{imaginary component}}{\text{real component}}$$

which for OP makes θ, $\tan^{-1} 3/4 = 36.9°$ and for OQ, $\tan^{-1} 5/2 = 68.2°$ or from the reference axis $180 + 68.2 = 248.2°$.

The technique can most easily be examined using the simple circuit of a resistor and capacitor in series as shown in Figure A4.1(ii). The capacitive reactance at the frequency shown $(-1/\omega C)$ is -100 ohms (capacitive reactance is always given a negative sign) so in complex notation the impedance (Z) of the circuit as shown in (iii) of the figure is:

$$Z = 200 - j100 \text{ ohms.}$$

From this the modulus of the impedance (modulus refers to the magnitude only):

$$|Z| = \sqrt{\left\{200^2 + (-100^2)\right\}} = 223.6 \text{ ohms}$$

$$\theta = \tan^{-1} \frac{-100}{200} = -26.6°.$$

Complex numbers can be added, subtracted, multiplied and divided. In all these operations it must be remembered that real and imaginary terms represent quantities which differ in phase and therefore must be kept apart.

From the above it is clear that when required, an impedance can be quoted in the form $R + jX$ where R is the resistance and X the total reactance. In this form it is known as the *complex impedance*. Only in the real part (R) can power be dissipated. The imaginary part (jX) indicates the phase difference between the voltage and the current. This part is either positive or negative depending on whether the current lags or leads the voltage. Accordingly for a purely resistive circuit an impedance diagram as for example A4.1(iii) would be reduced to a real axis only, conversely a circuit containing reactance only would be fully illustrated by the imaginary axis (not that such conditions are likely to arise).

Appendix 5

A HISTORY OF ENLIGHTENMENT

Early Experimenters:

1621 Willebrord Snell
(published his Law on the refraction of light)
1650 Pierre de Fermat
(developed the principle of least time)
1666 Sir Isaac Newton
(relationship between white light and the colour spectrum)
1678 Christiaan Huygens
(light as a form of wave motion)
1738—1806 Charles Augustin de Coulomb
(gave us his Law governing the force between charges at rest)
1802 Thomas Young
(through interference effects was able to prove wave theory of light)
1803 John Dalton
(introduced atomic theory of matter)
1811—99 Robert Wilhelm Bunsen
(developed grease-spot photometer and invented Bunsen burner)
1842—1919 Lord (J.W.S.) Rayleigh
(produced law for scattering of particles)
1862 James Clerk Maxwell
(published electromagnetic theory of light)
1820—93 John Tyndall
(showed that blue sky arises from the scattering of sunlight by dust particles)
1887 Michelson & Morley
(speed of light not affected by the motion of the earth)
1897 Sir J.J. Thomson
(discovered existence of the electron)
1900 Max Planck
(developed quantum theory and suggested existence of photons)

1905 Albert Einstein
  (explained photoelectric effect and later produced his mass-energy relationship);

thereon research into the intricacies of the atom continued apace, e.g.:

1911 Lord Ernest Rutherford
  (first considered the atom as a central nucleus with electrons in orbit)
1913 Niels Henrik Bohr
  (restriction of electrons to specified orbits)
1922 Arthur H. Compton
  (increase in wavelength of X-rays which have been scattered by electrons)
1924 Louis Victor de Broglie
  (developed idea of particles and the existence of waves of matter)
1925 Wolfgang Pauli
  (developed exclusion principle as a key to atomic structure)
1926 Erwin Schrödinger
  (wave equation for the hydrogen atom)
1927 Werner K. Heisenberg
  (published his uncertainty principle — impossible to measure simultaneously both the momentum and the position of a particle)
1933 Paul Dirac
  (spinning electrons behaving like tiny magnets);

then many others dealing mathematically in statistical wave mechanics.

Index

Please note following is a list of other titles that are available in our range of Radio, Electronics and Computer books.

These should be available from all good Booksellers, Radio Component Dealers and Mail Order Companies.

However, should you experience difficulty in obtaining any title in your area, then please write directly to the Publisher enclosing payment to cover the cost of the book plus adequate postage.

If you would like a complete catalogue of our entire range of Radio, Electronics and Computer Books then please send a Stamped Addressed Envelope to:

BERNARD BABANI (publishing) LTD
THE GRAMPIANS
SHEPHERDS BUSH ROAD
LONDON W6 7NF
ENGLAND